# TABLE OF CONTENTS

S0-ABU-315

## Close Up on the Supreme Court Extension Activities



## Landmark Supreme Court Cases



Copyright ©2001 by Prentice-Hall, Inc., Upper Saddle River, New Jersey 07458. All rights reserved. Printed in the United States of America. This publication is protected by copyright, and permission should be obtained from the publisher prior to any prohibited reproduction, storage in a retrieval system, or transmission in any form or by any means, electronic, mechanical, photocopying, recording, or likewise. Student worksheets and tests may be reproduced for classroom use, the number not to exceed the number of students in each class. For information regarding permission(s), write to: Rights and Permissions Department.

3 4 5 6 7 8 9 10   05 04 03 02
ISBN 0-13-054221-0

NAME ______________________ CLASS ______________ DATE ______________

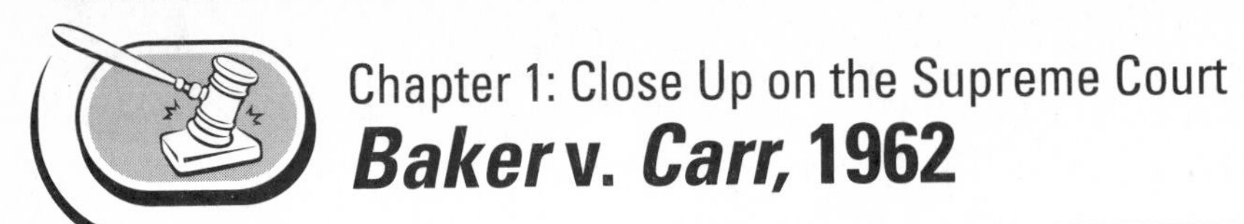

Chapter 1: Close Up on the Supreme Court

# *Baker* v. *Carr*, 1962

> ***Must voting districts be equal in population?***

## Case Summary

In the State legislature of Tennessee, representation was determined by a 1901 law setting the number of legislators for each county. Urban areas, which had grown greatly in population since 1901, were underrepresented. Mayor Baker of Nashville brought suit, saying that the apportionment denied voters of urban areas equal protection of the law as guaranteed by the 14th Amendment. The federal court refused to enter the "political thicket" of State districting, and the case was appealed to the Supreme Court.

## The Court's Decision

In a 6–2 ruling, the Supreme Court held that federal courts have the power to determine the constitutionality of a State's voting districts.

Justice William J. Brennan, Jr., wrote the majority opinion, stating that the plaintiffs' constitutional right to have their votes count fairly gave them the necessary legal interest to bring the lawsuit. He argued that the case did not involve a "political question" that prevented judicial review. A court could determine the constitutionality of a State's apportionment decisions, he wrote, without interfering with the legislature's political judgments. The case was returned to the federal court.

Justice William O. Douglas wrote a concurring opinion. He declared that if a voter no longer has "the full constitutional value of his franchise [right to vote], and the legislative branch fails to take appropriate restorative action, the doors of the courts must be open to him."

In a dissenting opinion, Justice John Harlan II argued that the federal equal protection clause does not prevent a State "from choosing any electoral legislative structure it thinks best suited to the interests, temper, and customs of its people." If a State chose to "distribute electoral strength among geographical units, rather than according to a census of population," he wrote, that choice "is...a rational decision of policy...entitled to equal respect from this Court."

## More on the Case

By holding that voters could challenge the constitutionality of electoral apportionment in federal court, *Baker* v. *Carr* opened the doors of the federal courts to a long line of apportionment cases. One year later, Douglas extended the *Baker* ruling by establishing the "one man, one vote" principle in *Gray* v. *Sanders*. In 1964, *Wesberry* v. *Sanders* extended that principle to federal elections, holding that ". . . as nearly as practicable, one man's vote in a congressional election is to be worth as much as another's."

Apportionment cases have become steadily more complex. Since 1993, the Supreme Court has reviewed various State and local efforts to design legislative districts in ways that would help minority candidates. The Court has invalidated those districts if race was a "predominant factor" in their design.

One such case is *Hunt* v. *Cromartie,* decided in 1999. In 1992, the North Carolina legislature created a district that connected several areas with many black voters. The new district was 160 miles long and in some places was no wider than the interstate highway. The Supreme Court found insufficient evidence to prove that the legislature had been racially motivated when drawing up the electoral district, and thus sent the case back to the district court for trial.

## Questions for Discussion

1. A major issue in *Baker* v. *Carr* was whether federal courts should have the authority to review the way a state legislature draws district lines for State elections. What are the arguments for and against allowing federal court review? Which do you find most convincing?

2. In the United States Senate, each State has two senators regardless of its population. Does this seem to contradict the 14th Amendment as interpreted by the Supreme Court in Baker v. Carr? Explain.

NAME ______________ CLASS ______________ DATE ______________



# *United States* v. *Eichman*, 1990

## Case Summary

Eichman and others were prosecuted under the federal Flag Protection Act for setting fire to American flags. Eichman and the others stated that the Act violated the First Amendment, and courts in Washington State and in the District of Columbia agreed. The United States Government then appealed to the Supreme Court.

*Is flag-burning "free speech"?*

## The Court's Decision

In a 5–4 decision, the Supreme Court held that flag burning was a form of expression protected under the First Amendment.

Justice William Brennan wrote for the majority. He rejected the government's argument that the law protects the flag's integrity as a national symbol. The law's intent, he stated, is to punish people who burn the flag as a way of communicating their ideas and beliefs. Finally, Justice Brennan refused to consider Congress's finding of a "national consensus," or agreement, against flag burning. "Even assuming such a consensus exists, any suggestion that the Government's interest in suppressing speech becomes more weighty as popular opposition to that speech grows is foreign to the First Amendment."

Dissenting, Justice John Paul Stevens argued that the government can put limited restrictions on expression if there is a legitimate reason for them that is unrelated to the ideas being expressed and if other methods of expression are available as alternatives. Justice Stevens felt those who might choose to burn the flag as a means of expression could also find other ways of communicating their ideas.

Justice Stevens commented, "What I regard as the damage to the symbol...has already occurred as a result of this Court's decision to place its stamp of approval on the act of flag burning. A formerly dramatic expression of protest is now rather commonplace."

## More on the Case

As a consequence of the Court's decision, the House of Representatives voted to adopt proposed constitutional amendments banning flag desecration in 1990, 1995, 1997, and 2000. However, the amendment has never received the necessary two-thirds approval in the Senate.

During the 2000 debates on the amendment, Robert Byrd (D., West Virginia), a senior and highly respected member of the Senate, announced that he had changed his position and now opposed the amendment. Although he continued to find flag burning "deeply offensive," he had concluded that the amendment would be out of place in the Constitution. "It is that Constitution," he said, "that provides us with the rights that all Americans enjoy...it isn't the flag."

The Senate Majority Leader, Trent Lott (R., Mississippi) disagreed. "The American flag is a sacred, basic, fundamental symbol of our nation's ideals, the symbol of those fundamental values for which we have asked our young men and women to fight and die," he said. "Allowing the desecration of our national symbol is not a sign of strength, it's a sign of self-indulgence."

## Questions for Discussion

1. Why did Justice Brennan refuse to take into account a possible "national consensus" on the issue of flag burning?
2. Should people be allowed to use parts of the flag as clothing? How might the Supreme Court have ruled on such a case, given its decision in *United States* v. *Eichman*?

NAME ______________________ CLASS ____________ DATE ____________

# Chapter 3: Close Up on the Supreme Court
# *Ingraham* v. *Wright,* 1977

***May schools use corporal punishment?***

## Case Summary

Two Florida students who were paddled in school brought suit in federal court arguing that the paddling was "cruel and unusual punishment" and that students should have a right to be heard before physical punishment is given. They lost in the trial court and at the Court of Appeals, and then appealed to the Supreme Court.

## The Court's Decision

In a 5–4 decision, the Supreme Court decided that public school students could be paddled without first receiving a hearing.

Justice Lewis Powell wrote the majority opinion. He pointed out that the Eighth Amendment's ban on "cruel and unusual punishment" had always been applied to punishment of convicted criminals. The Court therefore did not apply the ban to non-criminal contexts, such as school discipline. Finally, Powell wrote that "In view of the low incidence of abuse, the openness of our schools, and the common law safeguards that already exist, the risk of error that may result in violation of a school child's substantive rights can only be regarded a minimal. Imposing additional administrative safeguards as a constitutional requirement might reduce that risk marginally, but would also entail a significant intrusion into an area of primary educational responsibility."

Justice Byron White argued in dissent that the Eight Amendment does not contain the word "criminal," so the Court should not impose that limitation. "The disciplinarian need only take a few minutes to give the student 'notice of the charge against him and, if he denies them, an explanation of the evidence the authorities have and an opportunity to present his side of the story.'" Justice White quoted an earlier case to support his opinion: "The Constitution requires, 'if anything, less than a fair-minded school principal would impose upon himself' in order to avoid injustice."

## More on the Case

*Ingraham* is one of a series of cases in which the Supreme Court has struggled to find the proper balance between the rights of individual students and the needs of school officials to maintain order to protect the rights of students as a group.

The quote in Justice White's dissent about a "fair-minded school principal" comes from another student-rights case, *Goss* v. *Lopez,* decided in 1975. In *Goss* v. *Lopez,* the Supreme Court held that a student must be given effective notice and at least an informal opportunity to tell his or her story before or soon after imposition of a suspension from school.

*Ingraham* was later relied on by both the majority and the dissent in yet another Supreme Court student-rights case, *Vernonia School District 47J* v. *Acton,* 1995. In that case, James Acton, then a seventh grader, was not allowed to play football because he and his parents refused to consent to mandatory random drug testing—a policy that had been unanimously endorsed by parents in a meeting called to address drug usage in the school. The majority found that drug testing did not violate the Constitution. In dissent, Justice Sandra Day O'Connor disputed the majority's reliance on *Ingraham.* In her view, *Ingraham* gave schools "substantial constitutional leeway in carrying out their traditional mission of responding to *particularized* wrongdoing....By contrast, intrusive, blanket searches of school children, most of whom are innocent, for evidence of serious wrongdoing is not part of any traditional school function of which I am aware."

## Questions for Discussion

1. According to Justice Powell, to whom does the Eighth Amendment apply? How did Justice White respond?
2. Under what circumstances would drug testing of students be appropriate?

NAME ____________ CLASS ____________ DATE ____________



# *Printz* v. *United States*, 1997

## Case Summary

Jay Printz, a law enforcement officer from Arizona, sued to challenge the constitutionality of the Brady Act provision that required him and other local chief law enforcement officials (CLEOs) to conduct background checks on prospective gun purchasers. Printz and other officials won at the district court, but the Court of Appeals found the Brady Act constitutional. They then appealed to the Supreme Court.

*Should States be required to enforce federal law?*

## The Court's Decision

In a 5–4 ruling, the Supreme Court held that the Brady Act provision was unconstitutional. Justice Antonin Scalia wrote the majority opinion. He stated that early federal statutes did not suggest that Congress thought it had the power to direct the actions of State executive officials. Also, the overall structure of the Constitution implies that Congress may not direct State officials: "The Framers explicitly chose a Constitution that confers upon Congress the power to regulate individuals, not States." Finally, although it is the President's job under the Constitution to oversee execution of federal laws, "The Brady Act effectively transfers this responsibility to thousands of CLEOs in the 50 States, who are left to implement the program without meaningful Presidential control...."

In his dissent, Justice John Paul Stevens argued that the majority opinion misinterpreted Congress's power under the Constitution. Congress may not usurp the powers that the Constitution reserves to the States, but when it exercises its legitimate constitutional powers, its actions are binding on the States, and State officials must obey congressional instructions. He also argued that the absence of similar statutes in earlier times does not prove that Congress lacks the power to enact such laws now. "The Federal Government undertakes activities today that would have been unimaginable to the Framers."

## More on the Case

Although advocates and opponents of gun control watched the *Printz* case closely as it worked its way through the courts, the issue actually considered by the Supreme Court has had little effect on the gun control debate. The Brady Act itself required the Attorney General to establish a national instant background check system by November 30, 1998. The duties imposed on CLEOs, which were ultimately found unconstitutional by the Supreme Court, were part of the temporary process that Congress established until a national instant background check system was operating.

Under the national system in effect since November 30, 1998, a prospective buyer provides background information to the gun dealer, and the dealer calls an FBI office in West Virginia where an agent performs an immediate check. The FBI responds by telling the dealer to proceed with the sale, to wait pending further investigation, or to not sell to this buyer.

The FBI performed 372,565 background checks during the first two weeks of the new procedure. Less than one percent of the applicants were denied. Over three-quarters received immediate approval, while the rest needed more investigation before being approved.

## Questions for Discussion

1. Why do Justice Scalia and Justice Stevens both devote such large portions of their opinions to analyzing early American statutes and to reviewing the writings of the authors of the Constitution (the "Framers")? Does an examination of historical materials help the Court decide a case today?

2. How might Congress enlist the support of State and local officials, such as CLEOs, in congressionally-sponsored projects without violating the ruling in *Printz*?

NAME ________________ CLASS ________ DATE ________

Chapter 5: Close Up on the Supreme Court

# *Communist Party of Indiana* v. *Whitcomb*, 1974

## Case Summary

In 1972, the Communist Party of Indiana was denied a place on the presidential ballot because it refused to provide an affidavit, sworn under oath, that it did not advocate the forcible overthrow of the government. After losing a court challenge, the Party appealed to the Supreme Court.

*Can candidates be forced to sign oaths?*

## The Court's Decision

The Court held that the loyalty oath requirement violated the First and Fourteenth Amendments. Justice William Brennan wrote the majority opinion, which was joined by four other justices. He argued that, although older Supreme Court cases had held that advocating violent political economic change was so dangerous that the government could outlaw it entirely, many more recent cases had changed this rule to give more weight to free speech. Brennan further held that the Constitution largely gives the States the power to supervise elections, but they must exercise this power constitutionally. A State may not limit a party's access to the ballot or restrict voters' constitutional right of association merely because members of the party believe in something.

Justice Lewis Powell wrote a concurring opinion in which three other Justices joined. He argued that the majority reached the right result in the case, but for the wrong reasons. In Powell's view, the Court should not have considered the more complex question whether the Indiana oath was constitutional. Since in this case the Republican and Democratic Parties were not required to submit affidavits accepting the oath, he wrote, there was no justification for placing a burden on the Communist Party that was not placed on the other established parties. Powell concluded Indiana had denied the plaintiffs the equal protection of laws under the Fourteenth Amendment.

## More on the Case

The Supreme Court has considered other cases in which States attempted to exclude people from voting or to prevent them from running for elected office for a variety of reasons. In *Richardson* v. *Ramirez,* 1974, the Court ruled that California could constitutionally prevent convicted felons from voting. Justice Thurgood Marshall dissented from the Court's opinion, arguing that a State cannot "strip ex-felons who have fully paid their debt to society of their fundamental right to vote without running afoul of the Fourteenth Amendment." Although some people worried that convicted felons might vote to undermine the criminal laws, Marshall relied on *Whitcomb* to argue that potential differences of opinion or matters of belief cannot be used to exclude anyone from the electoral process.

In *Chandler* v. *Miller,* 1997, the Court reviewed a Georgia law requiring candidates for certain State offices to certify that they have received a negative result on a urinalysis drug test within 30 days before qualifying for nomination or election. Writing for the Court, Justice Ruth Bader Ginsburg found that the testing requirement unconstitutionally interfered with candidates' personal privacy. She relied on *Whitcomb* to support her argument that "States...enjoy wide latitude to establish conditions of candidacy for State office, but in setting such conditions, they may not disregard basic constitutional protections."

## Questions for Discussion

1. What are the arguments for and against allowing the individual States to set criteria for candidates for State elective office? Which argument do you find more persuasive? Why?

2. Given the outcome in *Whitcomb,* how would you have decided the *Richardson* and *Chandler* cases? Why?

# *Oregon* v. *Mitchell*, 1970

**Who decides who may vote?**

## Case Summary

Oregon, Texas, and Idaho brought suit in the Supreme Court against the United States and Attorney General John Mitchell to challenge the Voting Rights Act Amendments of 1970. They claimed that only the States, and not Congress, have the authority to establish qualification rules for voters in State and local elections.

## The Court's Decision

The Supreme Court held, with considerable disagreement, that the federal 18-year-old voting age requirement is valid for national elections, but not for State or local elections. Justice Hugo Black announced the Court's judgment in an opinion that expressed his own views. Four justices agreed with Justice Black that the Constitution gives Congress broad powers to regulate federal elections. These four justices, but not Justice Black, thought Congress also could do so in State elections. They argued that the States have no legitimate interest in excluding 18 to 21-year-old voters, and that the Equal Protection Clause supports the right of people in this age group to vote.

Four other justices agreed with Justice Black that Congress could not regulate the minimum age in State and local elections. These justices thought Congress also lacked the power to set the voting age for federal elections. They argued that under the Constitution, only the States have the right to set voter qualifications.

All justices agreed that Congress can prohibit the use of literacy tests or other requirements that discriminate against voters based on their race in all elections. In upholding the ban on literacy tests, the Court accepted Congress's findings that the tests tended to disqualify a disproportionate number of minority voters.

## More on the Case

The decision in *Mitchell* may look like a victory for the States, but it actually left them with a serious potential problem. Because the Supreme Court upheld the lowered national voting age in federal elections but not in State elections, States were faced with the complexity and expense of keeping track of who was allowed to vote in various elections. For example, a nineteen-year-old might be allowed to vote for President and Vice President but not for State officials who were up for election at the same time. In 1971, at the urging of the States, Congress adopted a proposed constitutional amendment setting a uniform national voting age of eighteen in all elections. The States promptly ratified it.

The Twenty-Sixth Amendment states:

> Section 1. The right of citizens of the United States, who are eighteen years of age or older, to vote shall not be denied or abridged by the United States or by any State on account of age.
>
> Section 2. The Congress shall have power to enforce this article by appropriate legislation.

This was not the first time a constitutional amendment was adopted in order to resolve a national voting issue. The Fifteenth Amendment, ratified in 1870, prohibits abridgment of the right to vote on account of race, color or previous condition of servitude. The Nineteenth Amendment, ratified in 1920, prohibits denial of the right to vote on account of gender. The Twenty-Fourth Amendment, ratified in 1964, restricts States from imposing a poll tax as a requirement for voting in federal elections.

## Questions for Discussion

1. Why did the issue in *Mitchell* produce such disagreement within the Court?
2. What was the reason for the Twenty-Sixth Amendment?

© Prentice-Hall, Inc.

NAME ______________________ CLASS ____________ DATE ____________

Chapter 7: Close Up on the Supreme Court

# *Nixon* v. *Shrink Missouri Government PAC*, 2000

*Can States limit campaign contributions?*

## Case Summary

Shrink Missouri Government, a political action committee, and Zev David Fredman, a candidate for State office, sued Missouri's Attorney General, Jeremiah J. Nixon, challenging the constitutionality of a Missouri law that limited contributions to candidates for political office. The plaintiffs lost in the district court, but won at the Court of Appeals. The case then went to the Supreme Court.

## The Court's Decision

In a 6–3 decision, the Supreme Court upheld Missouri's limits on contributions to candidates for State office.

Justice David Souter wrote the majority opinion. In *Buckley* v. *Valeo,* 1976, the Court had ruled that federal limits on contributions to candidates for federal office did not violate the speech and association provisions of the First Amendment. The main issue in *Nixon* v. *Shrink Missouri Government* was whether the reasoning in *Buckley* also applied to State campaign limits. Justice Souter noted that "there is little reason to doubt that sometimes large contributions will work actual corruption of our political system, and no reason to question the existence of a corresponding suspicion among voters." There was no real evidence that the campaign contribution limits prevented candidates from raising enough money to communicate their messages to the voters.

Dissenting, Justice Anthony Kennedy criticized the Court "for announcing a rule that suppresses one of our most essential and prevalent forms of political speech." He argued that the majority had failed to recognize the harm created by the ruling in *Buckley. Buckley* limited direct contributions to political candidates in federal elections without restricting the amount of "soft money" that political parties or interest groups could spend to support or attack a candidate's positions. This system gives great advantage to candidates who have the backing of established parties and support groups.

## More on the Case

Congress created the Federal Election Commission (FEC) in 1975 to administer and enforce the Federal Election Campaign Act (FECA). Part of the FEC's duties are to monitor compliance with FECA's limits and restrictions on contributions to federal campaigns.

*Buckley* v. *Valeo,* decided in 1976, was the Supreme Court's first consideration of the FECA's campaign contribution limits. *Buckley's* basic ruling was that Congress can limit federal campaign contributions, but cannot limit spending by the candidates or their campaigns.

*Nixon* was the Supreme Court's first decision on campaign contribution limits in over twenty years. When *Nixon* was argued, thirty-five States had limits on the amount an individual could contribute to a candidate running for State office. The Eighth Circuit Court of Appeals ruled that Missouri had not shown sufficient problems with corruption or influence-buying to justify imposing the contribution limit. If the Supreme Court had adopted the Eighth Circuit's reasoning, the constitutionality of campaign contribution restrictions in all other States would have been in doubt.

## Questions for Discussion

1. In deciding this case, how did the Supreme Court balance the right of free speech with the need for fair and honest elections? What other options were available to the Court in resolving these issues?

2. What did Justice Kennedy mean when he wrote: "It is our duty to face up to adverse, unintended consequences flowing from our own prior decisions"?

© Prentice Hall, Inc.

# *Miami Herald Publishing Company* v. *Tornillo*, 1974

## Case Summary

Candidate Pat Tornillo demanded that the *Miami Herald* print his reply to the paper's critical editorials. Under the Florida "Right to Reply" law, *The Herald* asked the State court to declare the "right of reply" law unconstitutional. *The Herald* won at the trial court level, but lost in the Florida Supreme Court, and then appealed to the United States Supreme Court.

> ***Do candidates deserve "equal time"?***

## The Court's Decision

Chief Justice Warren Burger's opinion, for a unanimous Supreme Court, found that Florida's "right of reply" statute violated the First Amendment. Justice Burger noted that changes had been made in the media since the First Amendment was ratified in 1791. It has become increasingly difficult and expensive to start a newspaper or to communicate a minority point of view to the public. Justice Burger concluded, however, that the First Amendment still prevents the government from ordering a newspaper to print something it did not wish to print.

Mr. Tornillo argued that the right of reply law did not restrict the Miami Herald's free speech because it did not prevent the newspaper from saying whatever else it wanted. Justice Burger noted, however, that the law "exacts a penalty on the basis of the content" of the paper. The penalty would be the time, materials, and newspaper space required to publish a candidate's reply. As a result, "editors might well conclude that the safe course is to avoid controversy. Therefore...political and electoral coverage would be blunted or reduced."

Justice Burger concluded that "the Florida statute fails to clear the barriers of the First Amendment because of its intrusion into the function of editors."

## More on the Case

The First Amendment is intended to allow expression of a wide range of ideas. The Supreme Court has ruled that broadcasting is special because only a limited number of radio and television licenses are available. In *Red Lion Broadcasting Co.* v. *FCC*, 1969, the Supreme Court concluded that this "scarcity" of broadcasting opportunities allowed the government to impose special rules on broadcasters to insure "fairness." A station in Red Lion, Pennsylvania, was required to give an author air time to reply to a "personal attack." The Court determined that the rights of viewers and listeners to hear both sides of the story was more important than the rights of the station.

However, the Court held in *Tornillo* that similar right-of-reply rules would violate the First Amendment if applied to newspapers. A critical difference is that the Federal Communications Commission (FCC) decides who will have the right to use the broadcast spectrum, so it does not violate the First Amendment to require those broadcasters to give fair access to those who they attack. In other words, "fairness" is one of the obligations that comes with the privilege of having a broadcasting license. The government does not decide who can publish a newspaper, however, so publishers cannot be forced to give access to the public.

In 1987, the FCC issued another fairness report which concluded that there were then enough broadcasters in the marketplace so that diversity of viewpoint was no longer an issue, and government intrusion into the content of programming was no longer justifiable. As a result, the FCC eliminated the fairness doctrine.

## Questions for Discussion

1. Does the decision in *Tornillo* mean that newspapers are free to print whatever they want about people?
2. How might the elimination of the FCC fairness doctrine have contributed to the rise of highly opinionated talk radio?

© Prentice-Hall, Inc.

Chapter 9: Close Up on the Supreme Court

# *Flast* v. *Cohen,* 1968

## Case Summary

*May taxpayers challenge federal spending laws?*

A federal court ruled that Flast and the other plaintiffs did not have standing as taxpayers to challenge the use of federal funds for religious schools. "Standing" is a legal requirement under which a person can only file suit if he or she has a personal stake in the outcome of the case. The plaintiffs then appealed to the Supreme Court.

## The Court's Decision

In an 8–1 decision, the Supreme Court held that the taxpayers who brought suit to challenge the constitutionality of federal taxing and spending programs do have the necessary legal standing to obtain federal court review. Chief Justice Earl Warren wrote for the majority, citing the earlier case of *Frothingham* v. *Mellon,* 1923. In that case, Warren wrote, "this Court ruled that a federal taxpayer is without standing to challenge the constitutionality of a federal statute.... In this case, we must decide whether the Frothingham barrier should be lowered when a taxpayer attacks a federal statute on the ground that it violates the Establishment and Free Exercise Clauses of the First Amendment." Chief Justice Warren noted that, in contrast to *Frothingham,* the current case of Flast was about a violation of the Establishment Clause of the First Amendment, which prohibits any government action leading to the "establishment of religion." The Court concluded that the plaintiffs were appropriate plaintiffs because they had sufficient personal interest in preventing the use of their tax money for this purpose.

Justice John Harlan dissented. He argued that a taxpayer may refuse to pay a tax or may sue for return of a tax wrongfully collected, but may not sue to "challenge the constitutionality of the uses for which Congress has authorized the expenditure of public funds."

## More on the Case

The Supreme Court revisited the issues in *Flast* in 1982, when the Court decided *Valley Forge College* v. *Americans United for Separation of Church and State.* Congress had authorized the Secretary of Health, Education, and Welfare (HEW) to dispose of federal "surplus property." HEW transferred a former military hospital to a church-related college.

Americans United and several individuals brought suit in federal court, claiming that the transfer violated the Establishment Clause and made unconstitutional use of their tax dollars. In a 5–4 decision, the Supreme Court ruled that these plaintiffs did not have standing to sue. Justice William Rehnquist noted that the plaintiffs objected to a decision by HEW and not an action by Congress, and that they alleged no concrete personal injury.

In his dissent, Justice William Brennan wrote that "It may be that Congress can tax for almost any reason, or for no reason at all. There is, so far as I have been able to discern, but one constitutionally imposed limit on that authority. Congress cannot use tax money to support a church, or to encourage religion." Justice Brennan argued that there is no practical way for a taxpayer to challenge an unconstitutional expenditure when the tax is collected. "Surely, then, a taxpayer must have standing at the time that he learns of the Government's alleged Establishment Clause violation to seek equitable relief in order to halt the continuing and intolerable burden on his pocketbook, his conscience, and his constitutional rights."

## Questions for Discussion

1. Under the rule developed in the *Frothingham* case, taxpayers do not have standing to challenge expenditures because their interests are too remote. How does this rule compare to the rule developed by the Court in *Flast* v. *Cohen?*
2. Why is "standing" so important to the Court?

© Prentice-Hall, Inc.

NAME ______________________ CLASS ______________ DATE ______________

Chapter 10: Close Up on the Supreme Court

# *Hutchinson* v. *Proxmire*, 1979

## Case Summary

Professor Ronald Hutchinson sued Senator William Proxmire for defamation after the Senator gave a "Golden Fleece" award to the agencies that funded the professor's research. The trial and appeals courts ruled that the Speech or Debate Clause of the Constitution (Article I, Section 6), as well as the First Amendment, protected Senator Proxmire from liability for comments in the Senate and in press releases and newsletters. Hutchinson then appealed to the Supreme Court.

***May Congress members be sued for their statements?***

## The Court's Decision

The Supreme Court ruled that the Speech or Debate Clause does not protect Members of Congress against liability for information they transmit by press releases or newsletters. Chief Justice Warren Burger delivered the opinion of the Court. Six other justices joined in substantially all of the opinion; Justice William Brennan dissented.

Read literally, the Speech or Debate Clause protects Members only for a "Speech or Debate in either House." Neither the language of the Clause nor the history of its application supports immunity for more than core legislative activities. The Chief Justice observed that newsletters and press releases may be useful for communicating with constituents and with other Members of Congress, but they are not part of the legislative process and are not entitled to the protection of the Speech or Debate Clause.

Dissenting, Justice Brennan wrote: "I disagree with the Court's conclusion that Senator Proxmire's newsletters and press releases fall outside the protection of the speech-or-debate immunity. In my view, public criticism by legislators of unnecessary governmental expenditures, whatever its form, is a legislative act shielded by the Speech or Debate Clause. I would affirm the judgment below for the reasons expressed in my dissent in *Gravel* v. *United States....*"

## More on the Case

The constitutional Speech or Debate Clause descends from a similar provision in the English Bill of Rights. King Charles II of England had been rumored to be plotting with the King of France to make Catholicism the religion of England. The Speaker of the House of Commons, Sir William Williams, accused Charles II in the Commons, a house of Parliament. In 1686, after James II became king, Sir William was charged with libel and was fined. James II went into exile soon after, and a provision was included in the English Bill of Rights guaranteeing freedom of speech and debate in the legislature "for the sake of one...Sir William Williams, who was punished out of Parliament for what he had done in Parliament."

Justice Brennan recounts this history of the English Speech or Debate Clause in his dissent in *Gravel* v. *United States,* 1972, a case he referred to in his dissent in *Hutchinson. Gravel* and *Hutchinson* are the leading Supreme Court cases on the Speech or Debate Clause. *Gravel* concerned Senator Mike Gravel's release to the public of a classified Defense Department study on Vietnam War policy. The press reported that the Senator had also arranged for private publication of the documents. A federal grand jury attempted to question an aide to the Senator. The Supreme Court held that the aide was entitled to the same protection as a Senator, but that there was no protection from being called to testify about the private publication.

## Questions for Discussion

1. How did the Supreme Court interpret the Speech and Debate Clause of the Constitution in *Hutchinson?* How does the decision leave members of Congress vulnerable to lawsuits?

2. Explain why Justice Brennan cited the story of Sir William and Charles II in his dissent to *Gravel.*

NAME ______________________ CLASS ____________ DATE ____________

Chapter 11: Close Up on the Supreme Court

# *Heart of Atlanta Motel, Inc.* v. *United States,* 1964

## Case Summary

The Civil Rights Act of 1964 prohibited places of "public accommodation" from discrimination based on customers' race, sex, color, religion, or national origin. The Heart of Atlanta Motel challenged the constitutionality of this provision and, after losing before a three-judge federal court, appealed to the Supreme Court.

> *Can Congress prohibit discrimination by private businesses?*

## The Court's Decision

The Supreme Court ruled that Congress had the power under the Commerce Clause to enact the prohibitions on discrimination contained in the public accommodations section of the Civil Rights Act of 1964. Justice Thomas Clark wrote the opinion for a unanimous Court. He reviewed testimony presented at congressional hearings showing that Americans had become increasingly mobile, but that African Americans were discriminated against by hotels and motels, and often had to travel longer distances to get lodging or had to call on friends to put them up overnight.

Justice Clark noted that under the Interstate Commerce Act, "...the power of Congress to promote interstate commerce also includes the power to regulate the local incidents thereof, including local activities in both the States of origin and destination, which might have a substantial and harmful effect upon that commerce. One need only examine the evidence which we have discussed above to see that Congress may—as it has—prohibit racial discrimination by motels serving travelers, however 'local' their operations may appear."

Justice Clark also found that the Act did not deprive the motel owner of liberty or property under the Fifth Amendment. Because Congress has the right to prohibit discrimination in accommodations under the Interstate Commerce Act, the motel "has no 'right' to select its guests as it sees fit, free from governmental regulation."

## More on the Case

President John F. Kennedy proposed the Civil Rights Act as a step toward ending discrimination based on race, color, religion, or national origin. President Lyndon B. Johnson eventually obtained passage of an even stronger version of the act. In addition to the provisions of Title II dealing with public accommodation at issue in *Heart of Atlanta Motel,* the Act also covers equal voting rights and discrimination by trade unions, schools, or employers, requires desegregation of public schools, and prohibits discrimination in the distribution of funds under federally assisted programs.

Title II of the Civil Rights Act contains a specific exemption for private clubs or other establishments which are not open to the public. Many cases have considered whether particular organizations are in fact private within the meaning of this law. For example, courts have ruled that YMCAs were not private clubs and that their rental of rooms brought them within the public accommodations provisions of Title II.

In *Boy Scouts of America* v. *Dale,* 2000, the Supreme Court considered whether New Jersey's public accommodations law could require the Boy Scouts to accept a gay man as an assistant scoutmaster. The Court found that the Boy Scouts is a private organization and ruled that a State may not require a private group to take actions or express points of view contrary to their own beliefs. New Jersey's public accommodations law infringed the Boy Scouts' freedom of expressive association and interfered with their right to oppose homosexual conduct.

## Questions for Discussion

1. Why did the government rely on arguments based on interstate commerce to justify its efforts to abolish racial discrimination?

2. How did the decision in *Heart of Atlanta* impact the Boy Scout case in New Jersey?

NAME ______________________ CLASS ______________ DATE ______________

Chapter 12: Close Up on the Supreme Court

# *Watkins* v. *United States,* 1957

## Case Summary

John Watkins was convicted for refusing to answer questions of the House Un-American Activities Committee (HUAC) about people he believed were no longer members of the Communist Party. He asked the Supreme Court to review his conviction after it was affirmed by the Court of Appeals.

***How broad is Congress's power to investigate?***

## The Court's Decision

In a 6–1 decision, with two justices not participating, the Supreme Court held that the congressional subcommittee had not given Watkins a fair opportunity to determine whether he could lawfully refuse to answer questions, and that his conviction for "contempt of Congress" was therefore invalid under the Fifth Amendment's Due Process Clause.

Chief Justice Earl Warren wrote for the majority: "The power of the Congress to conduct investigations is inherent in the legislative process.... But, broad as is this power of inquiry, it is not unlimited. There is no general authority to expose the private affairs of individuals without justification in terms of the functions of the Congress. ...Investigations conducted solely for the personal aggrandizement of the investigators or to 'punish' those investigated are indefensible."

Justice Thomas Clark dissented. He argued that the majority opinion did not appreciate the actual way in which congressional committees operated. He concluded that Watkins was properly questioned about matters that were legitimately within the scope of the subcommittee's topics. "So long as the object of a legislative inquiry is legitimate and the questions propounded are pertinent thereto, it is not for the courts to interfere with the committee system of inquiry. To hold otherwise would be an infringement on the power given the Congress to inform itself, and thus a trespass upon the fundamental American principle of separation of powers."

## More on the Case

The rise of the House Un-American Activities Committee (HUAC) also gave rise to more cases involving contempt of Congress citations. As Chief Justice Warren described in *Watkins:* "In the decade following World War II, there appeared a new kind of congressional inquiry unknown in prior periods of American history. Principally this was the result of the various investigations into the threat of subversion of the United States Government.... This new phase of legislative inquiry involved a broad-scale intrusion into the lives and affairs of private citizens....It was during this period that the Fifth Amendment privilege against self-incrimination was frequently invoked and recognized as a legal limit upon the authority of a committee to require that a witness answer its questions."

Although *Watkins* appeared to check the power of HUAC, Justice William O. Douglas later wrote in his autobiography that "the promise contained in the Watkins opinion was not kept. [Other cases] gave the House Un-American Activities Committee broad powers to probe a person's ideas and beliefs. In effect, they allowed the committee to subpoena anyone who had criticized the committee, and to examine all facets of his life, holding him up as a subversive or a traitor and, if he was man enough to defy the committee, to see that he went off to jail for his contempt."

## Questions for Discussion

1. For what reasons and on what grounds did the Supreme Court find Watkins' conviction incorrect?

2. The Chief Justice refers to the increasing number of "investigations into the threat of subversion of the United States Government" after World War II. Why was this so?

© Prentice-Hall, Inc.

NAME ________________ CLASS ________ DATE ________

Chapter 13: Close Up on the Supreme Court

# *Nixon* v. *Fitzgerald,* 1982

*May the President be sued?*

## Case Summary

A. Ernest Fitzgerald claimed that he lost his employment with the Air Force because he gave testimony before Congress that was critical of his employer. He tried to add President Nixon as a defendant in his suit, but Nixon argued that a President cannot be sued for actions taken while in office. The trial and appellate court rejected the President's claim of immunity, and the case went to the Supreme Court.

## The Court's Decision

In a 5–4 decision, the Supreme Court ruled that the President is entitled to absolute immunity from liability for damages based on his official acts.

Justice Lewis Powell wrote for the majority. He noted that the Court had never before ruled on the scope of presidential immunity. Many public officials have a limited, or "qualified," immunity that applies so long as they have acted in "good faith." Some other officials, such as judges and prosecutors, have been given an unlimited, or "absolute," immunity because of the special nature of their duties. Giving the President only qualified immunity, Justice Powell argued, would make his actions subject to review by the judicial branch and might compromise the separation of powers. Lawsuits could distract the President from his official duties. The scope of the President's authority and responsibility is so broad that it is not realistic to restrict his immunity. Powell wrote that determining "good faith" would mean that the President's motivations would have to be examined in each case, which would be highly intrusive.

Justice Byron White's dissent argued that the majority's rule was too broad. Under it, a President could "deliberately cause serious injury to any number of citizens even though he knows his conduct violates a statute or tramples on the constitutional rights of those who are injured."

## More on the Case

The Supreme Court revisited presidential immunity in *Clinton* v. *Jones,* 1997. Paula Jones sued Bill Clinton while he was President of the United States, accusing him of sexual misconduct when he was Governor of Arkansas. Clinton argued that the case should be dismissed, because the President has absolute immunity from suit.

The Supreme Court noted that *Nixon* v. *Fitzgerald* gave the President "absolute immunity from damages liability predicated on his official acts," but did not extend this immunity to actions that were clearly outside the scope of his presidential duties. The major rationale of *Fitzgerald* was to remove the possibility that the threat of litigation would make the President "unduly cautious in the discharge of his official duties." Jones's allegations involved acts that allegedly occurred before Clinton became President, so *Fitzgerald's* reasoning did not apply and Jones should be allowed to bring her case.

Finally, the Supreme Court acknowledged that the trial court judge would have the discretion to schedule the various aspects of the case to minimize disruption of the President's official duties. The Court ruled that it is not appropriate, however, to automatically require the plaintiff to wait until the end of the President's term in office.

## Questions for Discussion

1. Compare and contrast the two cases dealing with the issue of presidential immunity. Are the distinctions made by the Court valid?
2. Justice White's dissent argues that the majority's decision puts the President above the law. Do you agree with this argument? Explain.

© Prentice-Hall, Inc.

NAME ______ CLASS ______ DATE ______

Chapter 14: Close Up on the Supreme Court

# *Korematsu* v. *United States*, 1944

> ***Can groups' liberties be limited during wartime?***

## Case Summary

Fred Korematsu refused to obey the wartime order to leave his home and report to a relocation camp for Japanese Americans. He was arrested and convicted. After losing in the Court of Appeals, he appealed to the United States Supreme Court, challenging the constitutionality of the deportation order.

## The Court's Decision

The Supreme Court upheld the order excluding persons of Japanese ancestry from the West Coast war zone during World War II. Three justices dissented.

Justice Hugo Black delivered the opinion of the Court. He began with the observation that legal restrictions on the rights of a single racial group will always be "suspect" and that "courts must subject them to the most rigid scrutiny." However, they are not necessarily unconstitutional. The exclusion order imposed hardships "upon a large group of American citizens. ...But hardships are part of war....Compulsory exclusion of large groups of citizens from their homes, except under circumstances of direst emergency and peril, is inconsistent with our basic governmental institutions. But when under conditions of modern warfare our shores are threatened by hostile forces, the power to protect must be commensurate with the threatened danger."

Justice Owen Roberts wrote in his dissent that this "is the case of convicting a citizen as a punishment for not submitting to imprisonment in a concentration camp, based on his ancestry, and solely because of his ancestry, without evidence or inquiry concerning his loyalty and good disposition towards the United States." Justice Robert Jackson noted that comparable burdens were not imposed upon descendents of the other nationalities (German, Italian) with whom the United States was also at war.

## More on the Case

After the war, Fred Korematsu continued his efforts to clear his name. The ruling in *Korematsu* troubled jurists and civil libertarians because it suggested that basic civil rights could give way to prejudice and hysteria. Congress enacted the Japanese American Evacuation Claims Act of 1948 to provide some monetary compensation to citizens who had lost their homes or businesses during the internment. Ultimately, in 1983, Korematsu succeeded in persuading a federal judge in San Francisco to set aside his conviction for violating the wartime order.

Congress reassessed the internment in the early 1980s, and in 1982 and 1983 issued a report called *Personal Justice Denied* which determined that military considerations had not required the removal of Japanese Americans and concluded that the *Korematsu* decision had been "overruled in the court of history." In 1988, Congress issued a formal apology for the suffering and loss of property the internment order had caused, and in 1989 authorized reparations of $20,000 to each of the approximately 60,000 survivors of the internment camps. Many of those who were imprisoned had been farmers in California who were pressured to sell, at rock-bottom prices, land that is now worth millions of dollars. In 1998, President Clinton presented Fred Korematsu with the Presidential Medal of Freedom.

## Questions for Discussion

1. Although Justice Black ruled against Mr. Korematsu, his opinion acknowledged that cases of racial exclusion were difficult. Do you agree or disagree with his opinion? Explain.
2. The majority's decision in *Korematsu* was clearly influenced by the times in which it was decided. Under what circumstances—if any—is it appropriate for the justices to take current events into account in making their decisions?

NAME ______________________ CLASS ______________ DATE ______________

Chapter 15: Close Up on the Supreme Court

# *Goldberg* v. *Kelly,* 1970

> ***Must a hearing precede the cutoff of welfare benefits?***

## Case Summary

John Kelly and others sued when State and local officials terminated their welfare benefits without having given them prior notice and an opportunity to be heard. The plaintiffs won at trial, and the Commissioner of Social Services of the City of New York appealed to the Supreme Court.

## The Court's Decision

The Supreme Court ruled that the Due Process Clause gives welfare recipients an opportunity to present evidence and arguments to an impartial decision maker before their welfare benefits are terminated.

Justice William Brennan wrote for the six-judge majority. "...[T]he crucial factor in this context...is that termination of aid pending resolution of a controversy over eligibility may deprive an eligible recipient of the very means by which to live while he waits." The Due Process Clause of the Fourteenth Amendment therefore requires that some pre-termination hearing must be held, but it need not be a full judicial trial. Brennan concluded that constitutional safeguards require notice and the opportunity to appear personally or through an attorney, to present evidence, cross-examine witnesses, and make arguments.

Justice Hugo Black wrote in dissent that there were nine million welfare recipients in the United States, at least some of whom are not truly eligible for assistance. "...[T]he Court today holds that it would violate the Due Process Clause of the Fourteenth Amendment to stop paying those people weekly or monthly allowances unless the government first affords them a full 'evidentiary hearing' even though welfare officials are persuaded that the recipients are not rightfully entitled to receive a penny under the law.... I do not believe there is any provision in our Constitution that should thus paralyze the government's efforts to protect itself against making payments to people who are not entitled to them."

## More on the Case

Prior to *Goldberg* v. *Kelly,* welfare payments were widely considered to be a privilege or a charitable payment, rather than an entitlement. Justice Brennan stated, "From its founding the Nation's basic commitment has been to foster the dignity and well-being of all persons within its borders.... Welfare, by meeting the basic demands of subsistence, can help bring within the reach of the poor the same opportunities that are available to others to participate meaningfully in the life of the community.... Public assistance, then, is not mere charity, but a means to 'promote the general Welfare, and secure the Blessings of Liberty to ourselves and our Posterity.'"

The Supreme Court has decided a large number of cases involving welfare, Medicare, Medicaid, and other forms of governmental payments. In *Dandridge* v. *Williams,* decided a month after *Goldberg,* the plaintiffs claimed that Maryland's Aid to Families with Dependent Children (AFDC) program violated the Equal Protection Clause because it set a maximum grant size regardless of family size. The Court rejected this argument. Because Maryland does not have a limitless amount of money to spend on family assistance, it may set limits and make classifications that are reasonable even if they are not perfect.

## Questions for Discussion

1. Who has the better argument on requiring a due process hearing before termination of welfare benefits—Justice Brennan or Justice Black? Why?
2. How do you think the Supreme Court might rule on a challenge to State welfare programs that deny benefits to resident aliens or to aliens who have not resided in the United States for a certain number of years?

# *Agostini* v. *Felton*, 1997

## Case Summary

A federal district court and Court of Appeals ruled against New York City, stating that the city could not have public school teachers provide supplemental instruction to disadvantaged students at religious schools during regular school hours. The city then sought Supreme Court review.

**_Can federal funds be used to help religious school students?_**

## The Court's Decision

In a 5–4 decision, the Supreme Court ruled that a federally-funded program can give supplemental remedial education to disadvantaged children in sectarian schools without violating the Establishment Clause.

Justice Sandra Day O'Connor wrote for the majority. Justice O'Connor concluded that the program "does not run afoul of any of three primary criteria we currently use to evaluate whether government aid has the effect of advancing religion: it does not result in governmental indoctrination; define its recipients by reference to religion; or create an excessive entanglement. We therefore hold that a federally funded program providing supplemental, remedial instruction to disadvantaged children on a neutral basis is not invalid under the Establishment Clause when such instruction is given on the premises of sectarian schools by government employees pursuant to a program containing safeguards such as those present here."

Justice David Souter argued in dissent that the Court was improperly departing from precedents established in other cases. Previous decisions found that similar programs violated the Establishment Clause for three reasons: a program might use State-paid teachers and public funds for religious education purposes; it might give the impression of State-supported religion; and it might subsidize religious education by freeing up money that would have been spent on secular classes.

## More on the Case

Although the Court has traditionally interpreted the First Amendment to require a distinct separation between government and religion, the Court has also been sympathetic to government attempts to provide academic assistance to all students regardless of where they attend school. This tension has resulted in some significant developments—some might say inconsistencies—in case law.

*Agostini* was unusual in that the Supreme Court reviewed—and overturned—its own decision made in a 1985 case, *Aguilar* v. *Felton*. The Court agreed to rehear the case based on the petitioners' argument that the composition of the Court had changed; furthermore, the effects of the first ruling had imposed a huge financial burden on the school district. The earlier *Aguilar* decision had held that supplemental instruction by public school teachers during regular school hours violated the Establishment Clause. Justice Souter relied on this decision in framing his dissent for *Agostini*.

Federal and State governments have continued to look for ways to support non-religious education in parochial schools without violating the First Amendment. The Education Consolidation and Improvement Act of 1981 provided federal funds to local educational agencies for the purchase of computers and other educational equipment to be lent to public and private schools for "secular, neutral, and nonideological programs." In *Mitchell* v. *Helms*, decided in 2000, the Supreme Court ruled that this type of direct but neutral aid is constitutional.

## Questions for Discussion

1. Do you agree with Justice O'Connor or Justice Souter in this case? Explain.
2. How could the Court have ruled against the supplemental instruction in *Aguilar* yet upheld it in *Agostini*?

© Prentice-Hall, Inc.

NAME ______ CLASS ______ DATE ______

Chapter 17: Close Up on the Supreme Court

# *Rostker* v. *Goldberg,* 1981

*Should women be drafted?*

## Case Summary

In 1980, Robert Goldberg challenged the U.S. draft registration policy by bringing suit against Bernard Rostker, the director of the Selective Service System. When Goldberg won in federal court, Rostker appealed to the Supreme Court.

## The Court's Decision

In a 6–3 decision, the Court ruled that it was constitutional to register only men for the draft. Justice William Rehnquist wrote the majority opinion. He noted that "the question of registering women for the draft not only received considerable national attention and was the subject of wide-ranging public debate, but also was extensively considered by Congress in hearings, floor debate, and in committee. Hearings held by both Houses of Congress in response to the President's request for authorization to register women adduced extensive testimony and evidence concerning the issue."

Congress specifically determined that in wartime, the primary purpose of a draft would be to provide combat troops. "Since women are excluded from combat, Congress concluded that they would not be needed in the event of a draft, and therefore decided not to register them." He went on to say: "Men and women, because of the combat restrictions on women, are simply not similarly situated for purposes of a draft or registration for a draft."

Justices Byron White and Thurgood Marshall each wrote dissents arguing that Congress had improperly assumed there would be no need to draft people for non-combat positions. Justice White wrote: "I perceive little, if any, indication that Congress itself concluded that every position in the military, no matter how far removed from combat, must be filled with combat-ready men." Justice Marshall added that "the Government must show that registering women would substantially impede its efforts to prepare for such a draft."

## More on the Case

Social and political developments continue to affect the role of women in the armed forces. At the time *Rostker* was argued, about 150,000 women volunteers were on active military duty. The Persian Gulf War, in which 35,000 women served, demonstrated that the increased use of high technology military equipment had reduced the significance of physical strength. In 1991, Congress repealed the 1948 law barring women from serving on combat aircrews. This change opened up military career paths that had previously been closed to women. A *Newsweek* poll conducted during the Gulf War showed that about 50 percent of Americans favored including women in the draft.

In 1992, the Presidential Commission on the Assignment of Women in the Armed Forces recommended that women not be required to register for or be subject to the draft. A 1994 Department of Defense report observed: "Because of this change in the makeup of the Armed Forces...much of the congressional debate which, in the court's opinion, provided adequate congressional scrutiny of the issue...would be inappropriate today." The report concluded that it was not necessary to register or draft women, but noted that "the success of the military will increasingly depend upon the participation of women."

## Questions for Discussion

1. Much of the dispute between the majority and minority opinions related to Congress's determination that future drafts would be needed to fill combat rather than non-combat positions. Why did Justice Rehnquist accept that determination? Why did Justice White and Justice Marshall dispute it?
2. The justices all started with the assumption that women could constitutionally be excluded from combat positions. What arguments can be offered against this assumption?

© Prentice-Hall, Inc.

# *Reno* v. *Condon*, 2000

## Case Summary

The Driver's Privacy Protection Act of 1994 (DPPA) prohibited States from disclosing or selling a driver's personal information without the driver's consent. Data sold by the States had often fallen into the wrong hands and, in at least one case, had resulted in the murder of a woman who was being stalked. South Carolina, led by Attorney General Condon, sued to block enforcement of the act. The District Court and Court of Appeals ruled for the State, and United States Attorney General Janet Reno asked the Supreme Court to reverse this decision. The issue at the heart of the case was the safety of individuals and, in turn, their right to privacy.

*May Congress regulate States' business activities?*

## The Court's Decision

The Supreme Court ruled that Congress had the authority to enact the Driver's Privacy Protection Act (DPPA), because the act regulates the States as owners of motor vehicle databases that are used in interstate commerce. The Constitution, in Article I, gives Congress the power to regulate interstate commerce.

Chief Justice Rehnquist delivered the opinion for a unanimous Court. He reasoned that the personal identification information that the DPPA regulates is considered an item in interstate commerce. The States sell the information to companies which are themselves engaged in interstate commerce. "Because drivers' information is, in this context, an article of commerce, its sale or release into the interstate stream of business is sufficient to support congressional regulation." Rehnquist also refuted South Carolina's argument that the DPPA violates the Tenth Amendment, which grants all powers to the States that the Constitution does not specifically associate with the Federal Government. "The DPPA regulates the States as the owners of databases. It does not require the South Carolina Legislature to enact any laws or regulations, and it does not require State officials to assist in the enforcement of federal statutes regulating private individuals."

## More on the Case

In the 1990s, Chief Justice Rehnquist wrote a series of majority opinions regarding the powers reserved to the States. He authored *United States* v. *Lopez,* 1995, where the Supreme Court ruled that Congress exceeded its authority when it adopted the Gun-Free School Zones Act, which made it a crime to possess a firearm in a school zone. The Chief Justice concluded that possession of a firearm did not have an economic basis that would bring it within the scope of the Interstate Commerce Clause.

In *United States* v. *Morrison,* 2000, the Supreme Court invalidated the federal Violence Against Women Act. The act gave women the right to bring suit in federal court in cases of gender-related violence. Chief Justice Rehnquist wrote that "gender-motivated crimes of violence are not, in any sense, economic activity." Although violent crimes against women may ultimately have an effect on national employment and on the economy, that does not provide sufficient grounds for the federal government to regulate it under the Commerce Clause. "The Constitution requires a distinction between what is truly national and what is truly local....Indeed, we can think of no better example of the police power, which the Founders denied the National Government and reposed in the States, than the suppression of violent crime and vindication of its victims."

## Questions for Discussion

1. Why was the DPPA upheld while the Violence Against Women Act and the Gun-Free School Zones Act were not?
2. What constitutional issues was Justice Rehnquist describing when he spoke of the "distinction between what is truly national and what is truly local"?

© Prentice-Hall, Inc.

NAME ______ CLASS ______ DATE ______

Chapter 19: Close Up on the Supreme Court

# *Tinker* v. *Des Moines School District*, 1969

> ***May public schools ban political protests?***

## Case Summary

In 1965, John Tinker, his sister Mary Beth, and a friend were sent home from school for wearing black armbands to protest the Vietnam War. The school had established a policy permitting students to wear several political symbols, but had excluded the wearing of armbands protesting the Vietnam War. Their fathers sued, but the District Court ruled that the school had not violated the Constitution. The Court of Appeals agreed with the lower court, and the Tinkers appealed to the Supreme Court.

## The Court's Decision

In a 7–2 decision, the Supreme Court ruled that the students had the right to wear armbands to school to protest the Vietnam War. Justice Abe Fortas wrote for the majority. He first emphasized that students have First Amendment rights: "It can hardly be argued that either students or teachers shed their constitutional rights to freedom of speech or expression at the schoolhouse gate." While schools certainly have the right to establish rules relating to "the length of skirts or the type of clothing, to hair style,...[or] aggressive, disruptive action or even group demonstrations," this case does not involve any of those issues. "The school officials banned and sought to punish petitioners for a silent, passive expression of opinion, unaccompanied by any disorder or disturbance on the part of petitioners. There is here no evidence whatever of petitioners' interference, ...with the schools' work or of collision with the rights of other students to be secure and to be let alone. Accordingly, this case does not concern speech or action that intrudes upon the work of the schools or the rights of other students."

Justice Hugo Black dissented. He pointed out that the case involved a small number of students who refused to obey the instructions of school officials, and argued that allowing this behavior would have a negative effect on schools and on the country as a whole.

## More on the Case

Mary Beth Tinker eventually became a nurse and worked with the Veterans Administration. She later wrote that it was "a privilege to work with our veterans who had sacrificed part of their lives.... I work with a lot of paraplegics and quadriplegics, and some of them were injured in the Vietnam War... So I don't have any regrets about it at all. I'm proud to have been a part of anything that stopped the war."

The Supreme Court has dealt with other school cases since *Tinker*. In *Bethel School District No. 403* v. *Fraser,* 1986, the Court held that a high school student did not have the right under the First Amendment to use indecent language and sexual metaphors in a speech at a school assembly.

In *Hazelwood School District* v. *Kuhlmeier,* 1988, the Court ruled that school officials could regulate the content of the student newspaper in any reasonable way. The principal had deleted student articles about teen pregnancy and about the impact of parental divorce on students at the school. In both *Fraser* and *Kuhlmeier,* the Court emphasized that students in public schools do not always have the same First Amendment rights as adults in other settings.

## Questions for Discussion

1. Why would Justice Fortas have allowed the Des Moines school to regulate the length of Mary Beth Tinker's skirt, but not prevent her from wearing a black armband?
2. Why did the students prevail in *Tinker,* but not in *Fraser* and *Kuhlmeier?*
3. What facts did the Court take into account in reviewing the case and making their decision?

© Prentice-Hall, Inc.

NAME ______________________ CLASS ____________ DATE ____________

Chapter 20: Close Up on the Supreme Court

# *Illinois* v. *Wardlow*, 2000

## Case Summary

At his trial for unlawful possession of a weapon, William Wardlow argued that the police did not have grounds to stop him. The trial court rejected this argument and he was convicted. The Illinois Supreme Court reversed the conviction. The United States Supreme Court accepted the case for review.

***Does a suspect's flight from police justify a stop and search?***

## The Court's Decision

In a 5–4 decision, the Court held that police may consider a suspect's unprovoked flight as one factor contributing to "reasonable suspicion" justifying an investigatory stop. Chief Justice Rehnquist wrote for the majority. In *Terry* v. *Ohio,* 1968, the Court had ruled that the Fourth Amendment permits an officer to conduct a brief investigatory stop when there is reasonable suspicion of criminal activity. In *Illinois,* the Court relied on that ruling, as well as on precedents from other cases in which presence in a high crime area and unprovoked flight could be used by the police as factors contributing to "reasonable suspicion."

Justice John Paul Stevens wrote an opinion concurring in part and dissenting in part. He agreed with the Chief Justice that flight will not always justify stopping a suspect. There could be many innocent explanations: "A pedestrian may break into a run for a variety of reasons...any of which might coincide with the arrival of an officer in the vicinity." Some innocent people may nonetheless wish to avoid contact with the police. "Among some citizens, particularly minorities and those residing in high crime areas, there is also the possibility that the fleeing person is entirely innocent, but, with or without justification, believes that contact with the police can itself be dangerous...."

Justice Stevens noted that there was no testimony that the police cars were marked, that the other officers were in uniform, or that Wardlow realized they were police. There was no reasonable suspicion to stop him, and the fact that he chose to run does not provide the missing evidence.

## More on the Case

In 1989, the Court ruled in *United States* v. *Sokolow* that Drug Enforcement Administration agents had reasonable suspicion to stop a passenger at the Honolulu airport because he paid cash for his ticket, he was travelling under a false name, he was coming from Miami (a known source of illicit drugs), he had spent only 48 hours in Miami (although the round trip flight from Honolulu takes 20 hours), he appeared nervous, and he did not check any of his luggage.

Justice Thurgood Marshall dissented. He reviewed a series of often-conflicting factors that the Courts have relied on to justify a police stop: having one-way tickets and having round-trip tickets; taking a nonstop flight and changing planes; having no luggage, having a gym bag, and having new suitcases; acting nervously and acting too calmly. He also explained: "Because the strongest advocates of Fourth Amendment rights are frequently criminals, it is easy to forget that our interpretations of such rights apply to the innocent and the guilty alike."

## Questions for Discussion

1. Why did the Court not rule that flight alone will always justify a police stop?
2. The District Attorney of Alameda County, California, has commented that "*Wardlow* is an important case because it approves of detentions based on two circumstances that...are almost always indicative of criminal activity: (1) the suspect's presence in an area where street sales of drugs are a common occurrence, and (2) the suspect's flight from officers immediately upon their arrival." What would Justice Stevens or Justice Marshall say about this comment?

© Prentice-Hall, Inc.

NAME ______________________ CLASS ____________ DATE ____________

Chapter 21: Close Up on the Supreme Court

# *Regents of the University of California* v. *Bakke,* 1978

> *May public universities use admissions quotas?*

## Case Summary

Allan Bakke filed suit after learning that minority candidates with lower qualifications had been admitted to medical school under a program that reserved spaces for "disadvantaged" applicants. The California Supreme Court ordered the school, the State-run University of California, to admit Bakke. The university then appealed to the United States Supreme Court.

## The Court's Decision

A splintered Supreme Court affirmed the judgment ordering Bakke's admission to the medical school of the University of California at Davis and invalidating the school's special admissions program. However, the Court did not prohibit the school from considering race as a factor in future admissions decisions. Justice Lewis Powell, Jr., announced the Court's judgment. Four justices agreed with his conclusions as to Bakke individually, and four other justices agreed with the ruling as to use of race information in the future.

Justice Powell wrote that "the guarantee of Equal Protection cannot mean one thing when applied to one individual and something else when applied to a person of another color." He did not, however, prohibit schools from considering race as one factor in the admissions process.

Justice Thurgood Marshall argued that race could properly be considered in an affirmative action program, a policy of taking positive steps to remedy the effects of past discrimination. "In light of the sorry history of discrimination and its devastating impact on the lives of Negroes, bringing the Negro into the mainstream of American life should be a state interest of the highest order. To fail to do so is to ensure that America will forever remain a divided society. I do not believe that the Fourteenth Amendment requires us to accept that fate."

## More on the Case

The legal impact of *Bakke* was reduced by the disagreement among the justices. Because the Court had no single majority position, the case could not give clear guidance on the extent to which colleges could consider race as part of an affirmative action program.

In *Texas* v. *Hopwood,* 1996, a federal appeals court found that a University of Texas affirmative action program violated the rights of white applicants. The law school was trying to boost enrollment of African Americans and Mexican Americans. The court assumed that the *Bakke* decision was no longer legally sound, and explicitly ruled that "the law school may not use race as a factor in law school admissions." The court continued: "A university may properly favor one applicant over another because of...whether an applicant's parents attended college or the applicant's economic and social background....But the key is that race itself cannot be taken into account." The Supreme Court refused to review the appeals court decision.

Affirmative action remains a controversial issue in California. In 1996, voters passed the California Civil Rights Initiative, generally known as "Proposition 209," which prohibited all government agencies and institutions from giving preferential treatment to individuals based on their race or gender. The Supreme Court also refused to hear an appeal from a decision upholding the constitutionality of the law.

## Questions for Discussion

1. To what extent did Justice Marshall disagree with Justice Powell?
2. Would *Bakke* allow a public university to set aside spaces for economically-disadvantaged applicants? Applicants whose parents had not attended college? Applicants from single-parent families?

© Prentice-Hall, Inc.

# *Reno* v. *ACLU*, 1997

> ***May the government regulate the Internet?***

## Case Summary

In 1997, a group of organizations, including the American Civil Liberties Union (ACLU), challenged the "indecent transmission" and "patently offensive display" provisions of the 1996 Communications Decency Act. These provisions made it a crime to send offensive Internet material to persons under age eighteen. The district court found for the ACLU. On behalf of the Federal Government, Attorney General Janet Reno appealed to the Supreme Court.

## The Court's Decision

The Supreme Court invalidated both provisions of the Communications Decency Act (CDA) of 1996, because they violated the First Amendment's guarantee of freedom of speech. Justice John Paul Stevens wrote an opinion in which six other justices joined fully.

Justice Stevens reviewed the operation of the Internet and the difficulty of verifying the age of an Internet user. Justice Stevens pointed out several problems with the act: It did not define "indecent," it did not allow parents to authorize their children to access restricted materials, it applied "to the entire universe of cyberspace" rather than to well-defined areas. Moreover, the Internet is not a "scarce" commodity like the airwaves, so there is less justification for governmental regulation. Finally, the regulated materials do not just appear on the computer screen, but must be actively sought out.

Justice O'Connor concurred in part and dissented in part. She made an analogy to zoning law: "I view the Communications Decency Act of 1996 (CDA) as little more than an attempt by Congress to create 'adult zones' on the Internet. Our precedent indicates that the creation of such zones can be constitutionally sound." However, she agreed with the majority that the particular restrictions imposed by the CDA went beyond the permissible scope of legitimate zoning regulation and therefore joined the majority in finding the law unconstitutional.

## More on the Case

*Reno* v. *ACLU* was the Supreme Court's first case involving cyberspace. Justice Stevens attempted to place the Internet within the structure the Court has used to decide other media-related First Amendment cases. For example, because the Internet is not a "scarce" commodity like a license to broadcast a radio or television station, the government cannot regulate Internet content the way the Federal Communications Commission has supervised radio and television programming. The Court gave Internet communications the highest level of First Amendment protection, which traditionally has been available only to print media like newspapers and magazines.

Technological developments may also make *Reno* obsolete. For example, the Court's concern that the Communications Decency Act would discourage or prevent protected speech among adults was based in part on the lack of any effective way to determine the age of a person using the Internet. If child-blocking technology and age-check systems become more effective and are used more widely on the Internet, a law like the CDA might be upheld in the future.

## Questions for Discussion

1. If Justice Stevens recognized the legitimacy of Congress's goal of protecting children from contact with inappropriate materials, why did he write an opinion finding the provisions of the Communications Decency Act unconstitutional?
2. Should the Court make distinctions between different forms of media when they are asked to apply the First Amendment? Are the distinctions they have made valid?

© Prentice-Hall, Inc.

NAME ________________ CLASS ________ DATE ________

# Chapter 23: Close Up on the Supreme Court
# *Shelley* v. *Kraemer*, 1948

> ***May courts enforce discriminatory private agreements?***

## Case Summary

Kraemer and other white property owners governed by a restrictive covenant brought suit in Illinois State court seeking to block the Shelley family, who were African-American, from owning property. The plaintiffs lost at trial, but on appeal the Missouri Supreme Court reversed and ruled that the agreement was effective and that it did not violate the Shelleys' constitutional rights. The Shelleys then appealed the case to the United States Supreme Court.

## The Court's Decision

The justices ruled that a court may not constitutionally enforce a "restrictive covenant" which prevents people of certain race from owning or occupying property. Chief Justice Fred Vinson wrote for a unanimous Court. Justice Vinson pointed out that the Fourteenth Amendment prohibits discrimination by "State action," but the actors in this case were all individuals who had privately agreed not to sell property to members of certain races. Although the contract itself was private, the plaintiff in the litigation had sought the assistance of the State court in enforcing the contractual provisions. Vinson wrote: "[A]ction of State courts and of judicial officers in their official capacities is to be regarded as action of the State within the meaning of the Fourteenth Amendment."

He concluded: "We have no doubt that there has been State action in these cases in the full and complete sense of the phrase. The undisputed facts disclose that petitioners were willing purchasers of properties upon which they desired to establish homes. The owners of the properties were willing sellers; and contracts of sale were accordingly consummated. It is clear that but for the active intervention of the State courts, supported by the full panoply of State power, petitioners would have been free to occupy the properties in question without restraint." Accordingly, State judicial enforcement of restrictive covenants based on race denies the equal protection of laws in violation of the Fourteenth Amendment.

## More on the Case

Racial restrictive covenants were common at one time in many American cities. Many old deeds still contain these restrictions, though *Shelley* v. *Kraemer* made them unenforceable. Private discrimination in housing is now prohibited by Title VIII of the Civil Rights Act of 1968, as well as by statutes in most States and by ordinances in many municipalities as well.

In the 1960s and 1970s, when white residents in big cities sometimes worried about changes in the racial composition of their neighborhoods, a white family's sale of their house to a black family could be cause for neighborhood alarm. Unscrupulous real estate brokers learned that they could play on those fears by publicizing the sale, which they often did by placing a "Sold" sign prominently on the property in hopes of alarming other residents into putting their houses on the market, too.

Many cities responded by banning "Sold" signs completely. In 1977, the Supreme Court reviewed a New Jersey town rule banning both "Sold" and "For Sale" signs. The Court ruled in *Linmark Associates, Inc.* v. *Willingboro* that this ban violated the First Amendment because it "restricted the free flow of truthful commercial information."

## Questions for Discussion

1. Does *Shelley* v. *Kraemer* make it illegal for individuals to enter into contracts that discriminate on the basis of race?
2. Should private parties be free to do things (such as discriminate based on race) that would be unconstitutional if done by the government?

© Prentice-Hall, Inc.

Chapter 24: Close Up on the Supreme Court

# *City of Philadelphia* v. *New Jersey*, 1978

**Can States restrict undesirable imports?**

## Case Summary

Cities, including Philadelphia, and landfill operators, sued to challenge a New Jersey law that prevented out-of-State waste from being treated or disposed of within New Jersey. The trial court judge declared the law unconstitutional because it violated the Commerce Clause, by which the Constitution prevents States from regulating interstate trade. The State Supreme Court reversed, finding that the law had significant health and environmental objectives with little burden on commerce. The plaintiffs then appealed to the United States Supreme Court.

## The Court's Decision

In a 7–2 decision, the Supreme Court ruled that the New Jersey statute prohibiting importation of solid waste from outside the State violated the Commerce Clause. Justice Potter Stewart wrote the majority opinion. He quickly rejected the argument that the transportation of waste did not involve interstate commerce because the products are "worthless." Their movement from State to State constitutes interstate commerce, he reasoned, regardless of whether the waste products themselves have immediate economic value.

Justice Stewart noted: "Whatever New Jersey's ultimate purpose, it may not be accomplished by discriminating against articles of commerce coming from outside the State unless there is some reason, apart from their origin, to treat them differently." New Jersey's law restricts commerce from out-of-State in order to preserve New Jersey's remaining landfill. Justice Stewart concluded that this approach places the burden of New Jersey's conservation efforts on businesses located in other States, and thus violated the Commerce Clause.

Justice William Rehnquist's dissent argued that the Court has allowed States to enact "quarantine laws" that prohibit importation of harmful items. "I simply see no way to distinguish solid waste, on the record of this case, from germ-infected rags, diseased meat, and other noxious items."

## More on the Case

New Jersey, the most densely populated State, has made various attempts to solve the solid waste problem. After the failure of its waste-restriction efforts in *Philadelphia*, five counties built garbage incinerators. Although the new facilities were expensive, waste-disposal regulations called "flow control" required that locally generated waste be processed at local facilities. The flow-control regulations protected the counties from competition, so they could charge more for waste disposal, allowing them to pay for the new facilities. However, in 1994 the Supreme Court ruled that a similar New York flow control ordinance violated the Commerce Clause, because it prevented out-of-State companies from competing for local waste-disposal business. New Jersey's flow-control regulations were ultimately declared unconstitutional by the federal courts as well.

In *Oregon Waste Systems* v. *Department of Environmental Quality of the State of Oregon,* 1994, the Supreme Court further restricted States' waste-disposal options by ruling that a State may not impose a surcharge on the in-State disposal of waste generated in another State. The majority relied on the *Philadelphia* case for the proposition that "a State may not accord its own inhabitants a preferred right of access over consumers in other States to natural resources located within its borders."

## Questions for Discussion

1. Why did Justice Rehnquist disagree with the majority decision?
2. Is Justice Stewart correct in his determination that "waste" falls within the definition of commerce?

© Prentice-Hall, Inc.

NAME ______________________ CLASS ____________ DATE ____________

# *Board of Estimate of City of New York* v. *Morris*, 1989

## Case Summary

**Must local government follow the "one person, one vote" rule?**

Morris and others who lived and voted in Brooklyn, the most populous borough of New York City, claimed that the method of electing members of the Board of Estimate violated the Equal Protection Clause, because representation was not proportional to population. The trial court found for Morris. The Court of Appeals affirmed, and the City then appealed to the Supreme Court.

## The Court's Decision

The Supreme Court ruled that the composition of the Board violated the Equal Protection Clause, because each borough has equal representation despite wide disparities in population. Justice Byron White wrote for the six-judge majority. Three other justices concurred in the result but differed with specific parts of the analysis.

Justice White began by observing that the constitutional rule of "one-person, one-vote" applies to local government as well as to State and congressional elections. He then reviewed the functions of the Board of Estimate—which include a role in formulating New York City's budget of over $25 billion, plus management of city property, setting city salaries, and granting all city contracts—to show that the Board exercises significant legislative functions. The Board's "powers are general enough and have sufficient impact throughout the district to require that elections to the body comply with equal protection strictures."

The Court rejected the city's argument that the special structure of the Board was "essential to the successful government of...the City of New York...[because it] accommodates natural and political boundaries as well as local interests." Although the Court did not say that these political and geographical interests could never be considered, it held that they would not justify the large deviation in voting strength that was present in the case.

## More on the Case

As a result of the decision in *Morris,* New York City modified its Charter to eliminate the Board of Estimate as a governmental body. Many of the Board's powers were transferred to the Mayor; the City Council was expanded and its powers were enlarged as well. The role of the boroughs in municipal government was reduced.

Other localities have found creative ways to structure their elective bodies in compliance with *Morris* while preserving geographical and political boundaries. Delaware County is one of New York's sixty-two counties, with a 1990 census population of about 50,000 spread over nineteen towns. The smallest town, Bovina, had 550 residents, the largest, Sidney, had 6,667. The County is governed by a nineteen-person Board of Supervisors, with one member elected from each town. However, unlike the situation in *Morris,* Delaware County gave each Board member a weighted vote that closely matches the relative population in his or her town. For example, Sidney has about 12 times the population of Bovina, so Sidney's representative is allocated approximately 12 times the voting power. This arrangement was found constitutional under the *Morris* analysis by the United States Court of Appeals in *Roxbury Taxpayers Alliance* v. *Delaware County Board of Supervisors,* 1996.

## Questions for Discussion

1. According to *Morris,* do all publicly-elected bodies have to observe the "one-person, one-vote" requirement? Why or why not?
2. How did Delaware County account for the *Morris* case in setting up its Board of Supervisors?

© Prentice-Hall, Inc.

NAME ______________________ CLASS ______________ DATE ______________

## Close Up on the Supreme Court
# Recording Sheet

Fill in the chart below to help you keep track of important Supreme Court cases featured in your book and in any handouts you receive from your teacher.

| Case/Year | Decision |
|---|---|
| | |
| | |
| | |
| | |
| | |
| | |
| | |
| | |
| | |
| | |
| | |
| | |
| | |
| | |
| | |

© Prentice-Hall, Inc.

NAME ____________ CLASS ____________ DATE ____________

Close Up on the Supreme Court Landmark Cases

# *McCulloch* v. *Maryland,* 1819

## Historical Background

Throughout the early years of the Republic, the power of the Federal Government had continued to grow. By the second decade of the 19th century, cases pitting advocates of States' rights against those arguing for the supremacy of the National Government came frequently before the Court.

By the late 1810s, financial stability had become an issue of major national concern. The Democratic-Republican Madison administration and the Republican Congress had not renewed the charter of the Bank of the United States when it expired in 1811. When the War of 1812 pressed the economy of the nation, many banks collapsed. Those banks that survived, chartered by the States, lacked sufficient credit to spur postwar industrial growth. In 1816, Congress granted a charter to the Second Bank of the United States and supplied one-fifth of its capital of $35 million. Many local bankers, politicians, and farmers detested the bank, which they viewed as a symbol of the power and privilege of national moneyed interests.

## Circumstances of the Case

Among the States unhappy with the establishment of the Second Bank of the United States was Maryland. In those days, before the establishment of a single form of paper currency, local banks not only made loans but issued their own bank notes to serve as daily-use currency, instead of gold and silver coins. These banks enjoyed the lack of federal regulation and often pursued speculative policies. The Second Bank of the United States was authorized to regulate the issuance of currency by local banks, and followed a more cautious fiscal policy. Local banks thus looked to their State legislatures to restrict the Bank of the United States' operation.

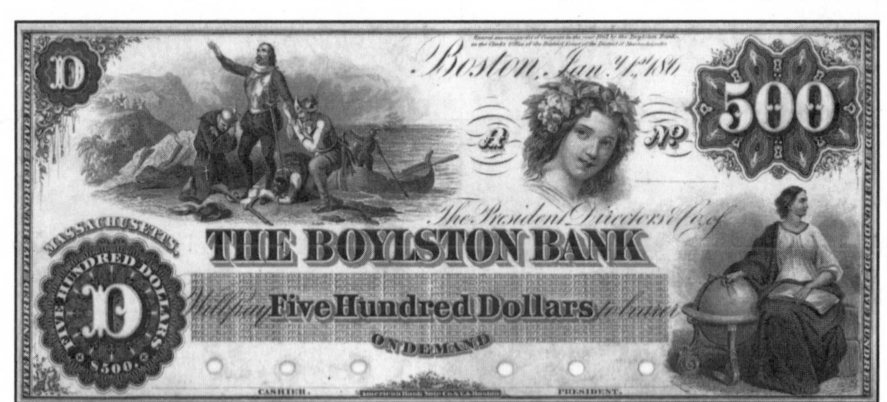


*Thousands of state-chartered banks, such as the Boylston Bank in Massachusetts, issued their own currency until Congress passed the National Bank Act in 1863, which led to the establishment of a uniform paper currency.*

The Maryland legislature responded to this action by levying a tax on all branches of banks "not chartered by the legislature"—a move aimed at destroying the Baltimore branch of the Bank of the United States. When called upon to pay the $15,000 annual tax, James McCulloch, cashier of the Baltimore branch, refused. McCulloch was convicted by a Maryland court and fined $2,500. He appealed the decision to the Maryland Court of Appeals, and, failing there, to the U.S. Supreme Court.

## Constitutional Issues

The case centered on Article IV's National Supremacy Clause and the Necessary and Proper Clause, Article I, Section 8. Was the Bank of the United States a "necessary and proper" exercise of powers granted by the Constitution or was the bank unconstitutional? Did the National Supremacy Clause prohibit State taxes on federal activities or was the Maryland tax law constitutional? Was the Maryland tax on only federally chartered banks a discriminatory action, antagonistic to the federal system?

## Arguments

**For McCulloch:** The creation of a national bank had been fully debated in Congress as a means for conducting the financial operations

© Prentice-Hall, Inc.

of the nation, and Congress had deemed its establishment "necessary and proper." Moreover, minute details of national operations cannot be specified in a document like the Constitution, which provides only a framework. As such, many legitimate powers of government are implied by, rather than stated, in the Constitution. The bank was a legitimate federal function with which no State may interfere. The Maryland tax on the national bank, therefore, was unconstitutional.

**For Maryland:** As a sovereign State, Maryland was vested by its people with all authority to regulate business and to tax institutions inside its borders. The regulation of banks was long accepted as a necessary means to prevent financial abuses. Since the Federal Government had created a number of statutes to regulate State banks, what should prevent Maryland from regulating federal banks? Furthermore, since no authority to charter a federal bank is included in the Constitution, the Bank of the United States was, the State argued, unconstitutional.

## Decision and Rationale

Speaking for a unanimous (7–0) Court, Chief Justice Marshall rejected the Maryland argument. The decision centered on Maryland's claim that because the Constitution was ratified by State conventions, the States were sovereign. Marshall refuted this claim, saying that the Constitution was the instrument of the people, not the States. Therefore, the Court asserted the supremacy of the Federal Constitution over the States. The Court also emphasized the importance of national supremacy. Marshall stated that "...the Government of the Union, though limited in its powers, is supreme within its sphere of action...."

The Court also rejected Maryland's argument that the Constitution did not explicitly allow for a national bank. Marshall's argument rested on this simple point: "...we must never forget that it is a *constitution* we are expounding." In other words, the Constitution was meant to be an outline of basic ideas, easily understood by the general public, and open to interpretation. Marshall went on to argue that while the powers of government are limited, the "necessary and proper" clause was meant to enlarge the ability of Congress to carry out its enumerated powers. He wrote: "Let the end be legitimate, let it be within the scope of the constitution, and all means which are appropriate, which are plainly adapted to that end, which are not prohibited, but consist with the letter and spirit of the constitution, are constitutional..."

Turning to Maryland's action in imposing the tax, he observed that "...the power to tax involves the power to destroy...," and on that basis, the Court ruled that Maryland did not have the power to destroy a duly constituted institution of the Federal Government.

© Prentice-Hall, Inc.

## Questions for Discussion

1. Based on Marshall's use of the "necessary and proper clause" in this decision, what do the words "necessary" and "proper" mean in the context of the Constitution?
2. What was the most important result of Marshall's decision in *McCulloch* v. *Maryland*?

NAME ______ CLASS ______ DATE ______

# Close Up on the Supreme Court Landmark Cases
# *Gibbons* v. *Ogden*, 1824

## Historical Background

The *McCulloch* v. *Maryland* decision in 1819 fanned the flames of controversy over States' rights and national supremacy. By 1824, Chief Justice John Marshall had reached the zenith of his historic tenure on the Court and was perfectly willing to consider the most difficult areas of law.

As the American frontier moved west and settlers pushed beyond the Appalachians into the Ohio and Mississippi river valleys, the question of commercial development became very important. In 1811, the National Government began construction of the great National Road to the west through the Cumberland Gap, and State governments engaged in a frenzy of canal building, capped by New York State's 363-mile wonder, the Erie Canal. Taxation and regulation of commerce through transportation was an important source of State income in the early years of the Republic, and interstate rivalries over rights to license and collect fees from transportation services became heated. Intense economic pressures mounted as some businessmen called for more free trade while other argued for States' rights in the management of internal matters of the State.

## Circumstances of the Case

In 1807, Robert Fulton's steamboat, the *North River Steamboat*, successfully navigated the Hudson River in New York. Fulton and his partner, Robert Livingston, negotiated a deal whereby the New York State legislature would grant them an exclusive, long-term contract to operate and license all steam-powered vessels in the waters of New York. Aaron Ogden obtained a license from Livingston to operate steam-powered ferryboats on the Hudson River between New York and New Jersey. Meanwhile, in New Jersey, Thomas Gibbons made his living carrying passengers by steamboat from the small town of Elizabethtown, New Jersey to New York City. Gibbons operated under a coasting license granted by the Federal Government, rather than under a license issued by either State. Because Gibbons had no New York license, Ogden asked the New York courts to issue an injunction forbidding him landing rights to the port of New York. The New York courts issued the injunction.

*A passenger steamboat from the 1800s.*

Gibbons appealed to the U.S. courts, arguing that his possession of a federal coasting license superseded the licensing requirements of New York State.

## Constitutional Issues

The major debate involved the meaning of Article I, Section 8—specifically, the Commerce Clause. What was the meaning of the word *commerce* in the Constitution? What exactly could the Federal Government regulate under that provision? Was the carrying of passengers a form of commerce? Should the word *commerce* be read narrowly (that is, boxes and barrels) or broadly (to include all forms of business relations for the purpose of trade)? Were the steamboat licenses of the State of New York in conflict with the National Government's authority to regulate commerce? If so, was the requirement for all steamships in New York waters to be licensed by that State constitutional?

## Arguments

**For Gibbons:** The Court was urged to take a broad view of the word *commerce*, which would subject passengers on interstate transports as well as other tangible items of commerce to federal regulation. Presenters argued

© Prentice-Hall, Inc.

that the federal coasting license superseded any New York regulation, because the Commerce Clause gives the Federal Government exclusive control over interstate commerce.

**For Ogden:** The Court was urged to take a narrow view of the word *commerce*. As a sovereign State, New York was fully empowered to regulate business within its boundaries. New York had granted Ogden a legal exclusive franchise, and anyone who wanted to operate a steam-powered vessel in New York harbor, with landing rights in New York City, would have to pay him for the right. New York's effort did not interfere with the National Government's effort to regulate commerce. The Federal and State governments had concurrent power over commerce.

## Decision and Rationale

Chief Justice Marshall delivered the opinion of a unanimous (6–0) Court siding with Gibbons. On the definition of commerce, the Court broadly declared, "Commerce, undoubtedly, is traffic, but it is something more: it is intercourse. It describes the commercial intercourse between nations, and parts of nations, in all its branches, and is regulated by prescribing rules for carrying on that intercourse."

The decision called Gibbons's federal license a legitimate exercise of the regulation of commerce provided in Article I, Section 8 of the Constitution. The New York State law creating a commercial monopoly was therefore void, since it conflicted with the regulatory power of the Federal Government in the performance of its constitutional responsibilities. The Court ruled that Gibbons must be allowed to operate within the waters of New York State.

As in the *McCulloch* decision, Marshall again asserted his belief in the supremacy of the Federal Government and its laws over those of the States. "...[T]he act of a State inhibiting the use of [waters or ports] to any vessel having a license under the act of Congress, comes, we think, in direct collision" with the constitutional prerogatives granted to Congress under the Commerce Clause. Thus, Marshall declared, "...the acts of New York must yield to the law of Congress...."

As a result of this decision, State-licensed monopolies on island waterways ended and business competition was encouraged. In 1837, the Court, under Chief Justice Roger B. Taney, would go one step further and effectively eliminate State-licensed monopolies across the board (in *Charles River Bridge* v. *Warren Bridge*).

The *Gibbons* decision established for all time the supremacy of the National Government in all matters affecting interstate and foreign commerce. The Marshall Court's broad reading of the Commerce Clause gave it a legal elasticity that was later extended to include federal regulation of railways, airlines, pipelines, television stations, telephone communication, and even racial segregation. Many constitutional scholars consider Marshall's opinion in the Gibbons case the Chief Justice's finest.

© Prentice-Hall, Inc.

## Questions for Discussion

1. Why would an advocate of States' rights want to have a narrow view, or strict construction, of the commerce power? Why would a national supremacy partisan want to have the Court make a broad construction of the commerce power?
2. What are some other areas of federal commerce regulation that have their foundation in the *Gibbons* case?

NAME ______________________ CLASS ______________ DATE ______________

# *Dred Scott* v. *Sandford*, 1857

## Historical Background

By the mid-1850s, sectional conflict over the extension of slavery into the Western territories threatened to tear the nation apart. The Kansas-Nebraska Act of 1854 destroyed the tenuous balance struck 34 years before between "free States" and "slave States" in the Missouri Compromise. Under the banner of "popular sovereignty," pro- and antislavery factions waged violent conflict for control of what came to be known as "bleeding Kansas" before that territory was admitted to the Union. With Congress sharply divided, reflecting the divisions in the nation, the Supreme Court took the unusual step of hearing the case of a fugitive slave suing for his freedom. Intended to be the definitive ruling that would settle the controversy threatening the Union for good, the case instead produced a divisive decision that pushed the nation one step closer toward the precipice of civil war.

John Marshall, in his time the single most influential advocate for strong National Government, had died in 1835. President Andrew Jackson appointed Roger B. Taney (pronounced Tawney). During his tenure as Chief Justice, Taney upheld strong national power, but with some modifications. Taney endorsed what is known as "dual sovereignty," which implies that State and federal governments are "foreign" to each other; each is sovereign in its own right. By 1857, Taney presided over a Court that had expanded to nine justices and was divided—four Northerners and five Southerners, including Taney, sat on the bench.

*An 1857 newspaper features a story covering the* Dred Scott *decision. Scott and his family are pictured on the cover.*

## Circumstances of the Case

Dred Scott was a Missouri slave. Sold to Army surgeon John Emerson in Saint Louis around 1833, Scott was taken to Illinois, a free State, and on to the free Wisconsin Territory before returning to Missouri. When Emerson died in 1843, Scott sued Emerson's widow for his freedom in the Missouri supreme court, claiming that his residence in the "free soil" of Illinois made him a free man. After defeat in State courts, Scott brought suit in a local federal court. Eleven years after Scott's initial suit, the case came before the U.S. Supreme Court.

## Constitutional Issues

Did a slave become free upon entering a free State? Could a slave—or a black person—actually be entitled to sue in federal courts? Was the transportation of slaves subject to federal regulation? Could the Federal Government deny a citizen the right to property (interstate transportation of slaves/property) without due process of law? Could an item of property (a slave) be taken from the owner without just compensation? And finally, was the Missouri Compromise a valid and constitutional action of the National Government? Could Congress prohibit slavery in a territory or delegate that power to a territory's legislature?

## Arguments

**For Dred Scott:** When a person enters a free State or territory, the free status overrides the previous condition of servitude. Since slavery was forbidden in the free States and territories by federal and State laws, Dred Scott became free when he entered Illinois and Wisconsin.

© Prentice-Hall, Inc.

# *Dred Scott* v. *Sandford*, 1857

**For Sandford:** To deprive a person of property (in this case, Dred Scott) without due process or just compensation violated the 5th Amendment, which states that "No person shall be... deprived of life, liberty or property, without due process of law; nor shall private property be taken for public use, without just compensation." Dred Scott was still a slave and no master's property rights could be limited or taken away by a State or federal law.

## Decision and Rationale

The Court decided 7–2 in favor of the slave owner. Every justice submitted an individual opinion justifying his position, with Chief Justice Taney's being the most influential.

According to Taney, African Americans, be they slave or free, were not citizens. As a slave, moreover, Scott was property and had no right to bring suit in federal courts. "In regard to the issue of Scott's becoming free when he moved to the free State of Illinois," Taney wrote, "the laws of the State in which the petitioner was currently resident, namely the slave State of Missouri, should apply."

Of far more serious consequence, the Court also struck down the Missouri Compromise as unconstitutional, because it deprived property owners (slave owners) of the right to take their property anywhere in the United States, thus "depriving them of life, liberty and property under the 5th Amendment." Any line, or law, that limited the right of slave owners to utilize their property was unconstitutional. Taney then ruled that the Congress could not extend to any territorial governments powers that it did not possess (in this case, the power to limit slavery). By declaring the Missouri Compromise unconstitutional, Taney not only destroyed one of the delicate compromises that had kept the union together for nearly four decades but also rejected the principle of popular sovereignty. Popular sovereignty, which held that territories could decide whether or not to allow slavery for themselves, had been strongly advocated by Stephen Douglas as the solution to the controversies in the federal territories that dominated the 1850s. This disallowance of popular sovereignty contributed to the national disorder over the spread of slavery.

The *Dred Scott* decision unleashed a storm of protest against the Court and the administration of President Buchanan, which supported the decision. The justices' plans to make a definitive ruling that would settle the controversy over slavery backfired as Republicans charged that a "Slave Power" conspiracy extended into the highest reaches of government. Violent struggles continued in the Kansas and Nebraska territories, where "free soil" and proslavery guerilla bands terrorized each other. A major landmark on the road to the Civil War, the *Dred Scott* decision was overturned with the adoption of the 13th and 14th amendments to the Constitution in 1865 and 1868. These amendments ended slavery and established firmly the citizenship of all persons, regardless of race, creed, or previous condition of servitude. As for Dred Scott, two months after the Supreme Court's decision, Emerson's widow sold Scott and his family to the Blow family, who freed them in May of 1857.

## Questions for Discussion

1. How do you account for (or explain) the Court's decision in *Dred Scott* v. *Sandford*?
2. Once Taney ruled that Scott did not have a right to bring a lawsuit, he could have simply dismissed the case. Why did he decide to deal with the issue of slavery in federal territories?

© Prentice-Hall, Inc.

Close Up on the Supreme Court Landmark Cases

# *The Civil Rights Cases,* 1883

## Historical Background

Between 1866 and 1875, Congress passed several civil rights acts to implement the 13th and 14th amendments. One was the Civil Rights Act of 1875, which imposed various criminal penalties against private businesses that practiced racial discrimination. Penalties were imposed on any owner of a public establishment or conveyance who practiced racial discrimination in the conduct of his or her business. Many Northerners and Southerners opposed to Reconstruction saw the law as an infringement of personal freedom of choice.

By the 1870s, various white supremacist groups, including the Ku Klux Klan, were using both nonviolent and violent means throughout the South to influence politics and intimidate African Americans. In 1877, when withdrawal of federal troops brought the Reconstruction period to a close, Southern legislatures began to pass laws and establish practices which created separate societies for whites and African Americans.

*The Civil Rights Act of 1875 was declared unconstitutional and legal segregation continued through the first half of the 20th century.*

## Circumstances of the Case

A number of cases involving application of the federal law were collected in this case and presented to the Supreme Court during the term 1882–1883. African-American citizens protested their exclusion from a hotel dining room in Topeka, Kansas; from the opera in New York City; from the better seats of a San Francisco theater; and from a car set aside for ladies on a train.

## Constitutional Issues

The case examined the constitutionality of the Civil Rights Act of 1875 in light of the Equal Protection Clause of the 14th Amendment. Did the Act of 1875 violate the Constitution? Was the conduct of business by a private person subject to the Equal Protection Clause of the 14th Amendment? Did the amendment prohibit State governments from discriminating, but *permit* private persons to discriminate under "freedom of choice" (that is, "We reserve the right to refuse service to anyone")? What protections did the 13th and 14th amendments provide for citizens?

## Arguments

**For eliminating private segregation:** The Civil Rights Act of 1875 was constitutional. The 13th and 14th amendments were clearly intended to "remove the last vestiges of slavery" from America. To permit private discrimination would be to "permit the badges and incidents of slavery" to linger in the South. The Federal Government had the authority to protect citizens from private and State actions that deprived them of their rights.

**For private segregation:** The intent and purpose of the 14th Amendment was to prevent discrimination in any form by the State governments. The amendment declares, "...nor shall any State deprive citizens of life, liberty or property without due process of law, nor deny any person within its jurisdiction the equal protection

© Prentice-Hall, Inc.

NAME ______________ CLASS ______________ DATE ______________



# The Civil Rights Cases, 1883

of the laws...." This is clearly and precisely *not* a limit on *private* action. It speaks to State action only. The Civil Rights Act was, therefore, unconstitutional and interfered with the private rights of citizens to use, manage, and protect their businesses and property. Private citizens have a right to decide the conditions under which they operate their businesses. Outside interference (that is, federal intervention) would amount to tyranny.

## Decision and Rationale

The 8–1 decision of the Court was delivered by Justice Joseph P. Bradley, with John Marshall Harlan of Kentucky alone in dissent. The Court decided that the Civil Rights Act of 1875 was unconstitutional. Neither the 13th nor the 14th amendment empowers the Congress to legislate in matters of racial discrimination in the private sector, Bradley wrote. "The 13th Amendment has respect, not to distinctions of race...but to slavery...." The 14th Amendment, he continued, applied to State, not private, actions; furthermore, the abridgment of rights presented in this case are to be considered as "ordinary civil injur[ies]" rather than the imposition of badges of slavery.

Bradley commented that "individual invasion of individual rights is not the subject-matter of the [14th] Amendment. It has a deeper and broader scope. It nullifies and makes void all state legislation, and state action of every kind, which impairs the privileges and immunities of citizens of the United States, or which injures them in life, liberty or property without due process of law, or which denies to any of them the equal protection of the laws." Therefore, the Court limited the impact of the Equal Protection Clause of the 14th Amendment.

Segregation by race in the private sector was given tacit approval by the Court. "Whites only" signs had begun to appear across the South by this time, and in the North as well. This decision was one of several which gave legal standing to efforts intended to return to the social order of pre-Civil War days. The major decision on segregation in America came 13 years later in *Plessy* v. *Ferguson*, 1896, when the "separate but equal" doctrine was seen as providing "equal protection of the laws" to African Americans. Justice Harlan, the lone dissenter in the *Civil Rights Cases*, as he was to be later on *Plessy*, made a point in the latter case whose echo is still heard today: "The Constitution is color-blind: it neither knows nor tolerates classes among citizens." Seventy-one years would pass after his first dissent, however, before a majority of the Supreme Court embraced Harlan's interpretation.

© Prentice-Hall, Inc.

## Questions for Discussion

1. Both the *Dred Scott* case and the *Civil Rights Cases* contain a line of reasoning that defends property rights over individual rights. Compare the reasoning in the two cases by examining the central statement of the Court's decision in the *Civil Rights Cases*. Why would this be called a "narrow construction" of the Constitution?
2. Supporters of the Civil Rights Act of 1875 hoped to remove the last "badges and incidents of slavery" from the South. Why would they think that the discrimination in these cases represented a "badge or incident" of slavery?
3. Should private behavior be subject to government regulation? What rule or guideline would you write for such regulation? How would your rule have applied to actions of the Ku Klux Klan in 1885?

NAME ______ CLASS ______ DATE ______

Close Up on the Supreme Court Landmark Cases

# *Plessy* v. *Ferguson*, 1896

## Historical Background

In the aftermath of Reconstruction, which ended in 1877, the Southern State governments again became—as they remained in the North— "white man's governments." The new State legislatures enacted Jim Crow laws to legally segregate the races and impose second-class citizenship upon African Americans. Enforced by criminal penalties, these laws created separate schools, parks, waiting rooms, and other segregated public accommodations. In its ruling in the *Civil Rights Cases* of 1883, the Court made clear that the Equal Protection Clause of the 14th Amendment provided no guarantee against private segregation. It would now be asked to rule on what protection the 14th Amendment offered in matters of public segregation.

In 1890, the Louisiana legislature passed a law requiring railroads to separate passengers on the basis of race. Trains that had two or more passenger cars were required to have designated seating for different races. If there was only one passenger car in a train, these cars were to be divided by a curtain or some other form of partition. A State fine of $25 or up to 20 days in jail was the penalty for sitting in the wrong compartment.

Timidity in the protection of individual rights—as reflected in the *Civil Rights Cases* decision—was a dominant characteristic of the late 19th-century Court. Attacks on its authority after the infamous *Dred Scott* decision in 1857 still plagued the bench and reinforced its regressive tendencies.

## Circumstances of the Case

Homer Adolph Plessy was a successful Louisiana businessman living in Baton Rouge. Comfortable in the society of both racial groups, Plessy had had one African-American grandparent. Although he did not consider himself African American, Louisiana law defined him as "octaroon"—one-eighth African American.

Plessy, acting on behalf of a committee that had been formed to challenge Jim Crow laws, intentionally broke the law in order to initiate a case. Returning by rail from New Orleans to Baton Rouge, Plessy was asked by railroad officials to sit in the segregated area of the train. He refused. Arrested and charged, Plessy petitioned the Louisiana Supreme Court for a writ against Ferguson, the trial court judge, to stop the proceedings against him for criminal violation of the State law. But the Louisiana State Supreme Court refused. Convicted and fined, Plessy then appealed to the Supreme Court of the United States.

## Constitutional Issues

The arguments in the case revolved around the 13th Amendment and the Equal Protection Clause of the 14th Amendment. Did the Louisiana law requiring segregated seating violate Plessy's "equal protection" under the law? Was a State law requiring separate accommodations on a public conveyance for whites and African Americans a violation of equal protection? Should the State law be ruled unconstitutional and Plessy's conviction overturned? Or would "separate but equal" facilities meet the standard of the 14th Amendment?

*Segregation on public buses continued until 1956 when it was banned by the Supreme Court.*

© Prentice-Hall, Inc.

NAME ______________________ CLASS ____________ DATE ____________

Close Up on the Supreme Court Landmark Cases

# *Plessy* v. *Ferguson*, 1896

## Arguments

**For Plessy:** Segregated facilities violate the Equal Protection Clause. As a fully participating citizen, Plessy should not have been denied any rights of citizenship. He should not have been required to give up any public right or access. The Louisiana law violated the Equal Protection Clause and was, therefore, unconstitutional.

**For the State of Louisiana:** It is the right of each State to make rules to protect public safety. Segregated facilities reflected the public will in Louisiana. A separate but equal facility provided the protections required by the 14th Amendment and satisfied the demands of white citizens as well. If *The Civil Rights Cases* of 1883 made clear that segregation in private matters is of no concern to government, why should a State legislature be prohibited from enacting public segregation statutes?

## Decision and Rationale

Justice Henry B. Brown of Michigan delivered the 7–1 decision of the Court that upheld the Louisiana law requiring segregation. Brown noted that the law did not violate either the 13th or 14th Amendments. He stated that the 13th Amendment applied only to slavery, and the 14th amendment was not intended to give African Americans social equality but only political and civil equality with white people.

Using a line of reasoning that would echo across the next 60 years of political debate and Court opinion, Brown wrote that "Legislation is powerless to eradicate racial instincts or to abolish distinctions based upon physical differences...." In other words, legislation cannot change public attitudes, "and the attempt to do so can only result in accentuating the difficulties of the present situation," Brown wrote. Reflecting the common bias of the majority of the country at the time, Brown argued that "If the civil and political rights of both races be equal, one cannot be inferior to the other civilly or politically. If one race be inferior to the other socially, the Constitution of the United States cannot put them upon the same plane." The Court declared the Louisiana law a reasonable exercise of the State's "police power," enacted for the promotion of the public good.

In the key passage of the opinion, the Court stated that segregation was legal and constitutional as long as "facilities were equal." Thus the "separate but equal doctrine" that would keep America divided along racial lines for over half a century longer came into being.

Somewhat ironically, while Brown, a Northerner, justified the segregation of the races, Justice John Marshall Harlan, a Southerner from Kentucky, made a lone, resounding, and prophetic dissent. "The Thirteenth Amendment...struck down the institution of slavery [and]...decreed universal civil freedom," Harlan declared. "Our Constitution is color-blind and neither knows nor tolerates classes among citizens." Harlan's dissent became the main theme of the unanimous decision of the Court in *Brown* v. *Board of Education* in 1954.

No great national protest followed in the wake of the Plessy decision. Segregation was an issue shunted off to the corner of our national life, and would remain so for nearly 60 years.

© Prentice-Hall, Inc.

## Questions for Discussion

1. Reread the decision. Examine the quoted material. Consider the logic of the Court in determining that "separation" was not a violation of the 14th Amendment. Can you find any logical flaw? Explain.
2. To what extent would it be correct to explain the *Plessy* decision as an act of reconciliation aimed toward the South and its States' rights doctrine?

NAME ______________________ CLASS __________ DATE __________



# *Schenck* v. *United States*, 1919

## Historical Background

A major effort to promote national unity accompanied America's involvement (1917–1918) in World War I. As a part of this effort, Congress enacted a number of laws severely restricting 1st Amendment freedoms to curb antiwar dissent. In 1917, Congress passed the Espionage Act, which set stiff penalties for uttering and circulating "false" statements intended to interfere with the war effort. Any effort to cause unrest in the military forces or to interfere with the draft was forbidden. In 1918, Congress passed a Sedition Act—the first such act in 120 years—which made it a crime to interfere with the sale of government securities (war bonds) and also prohibited saying or publishing anything disrespectful to the government of the United States.

The Committee on Public Information, a collection of leading writers and journalists, effectively functioned as a propaganda arm of the government, distributing some 75 million pieces of literature on behalf of the war effort from 1917 to 1918. But the strict conformity demanded by the government in wartime invited an element of hysteria. Dissenters were often forcibly silenced and jailed for their views. Among the best organized organs of dissent against the war was the Socialist party. Its leader, Eugene V. Debs, was sentenced to 10 years in prison for his statement that while the "master classes" caused the war, the "subject classes" would have to fight it. A Butte, Montana, mob dragged antiwar labor-organizer Frank Little through the streets before they hung him from a railroad trestle. In Washington, the House of Representatives refused to allow Milwaukee representative Victor Berger, a Socialist elected in 1918, to take his seat, despite his service in that chamber from 1911 to 1913. Berger, too, had been jailed for his antiwar views. Berger was allowed back into the chamber from 1923 to 1929.

*A poster encouraging Americans to enlist in the armed forces during World War I.*

## Circumstances of the Case

Charles Schenck was the general secretary of the Socialist Party of America. Socialists believed that the war had been caused by and would benefit only the rich, while causing suffering and death for the thousands of poor and working-class soldiers who would do the actual fighting in Europe. Party officials not only opposed the war, they urged American workers to oppose the war as well.

Schenck participated in many antiwar activities in violation of the Espionage Act, including the mailing of about 15,000 leaflets urging draftees and soldiers to resist the draft. He was arrested and charged with "causing and attempting to cause insubordination in the military and naval forces of the United States" and with disturbing the draft. He was arrested, tried, convicted, and sentenced to prison for violating the Espionage Act of 1917, and he appealed his case to the Supreme Court.

## Constitutional Issues

Were Schenck's political statements protected by the free speech section of the 1st Amendment? What was the meaning of the 1st Amendment's statement that "Congress shall make no law...abridging the freedom of

© Prentice-Hall, Inc.

# *Schenck* v. *United States,* 1919

speech"? Were there different standards for protected political speech during peacetime and in war? Was the Espionage Act constitutional or did it violate the 1st Amendment? Should Schenck remain in prison?

## Arguments

**For Schenck:** The Espionage Act was unconstitutional. Schenck and the Socialist party were persecuted for opposing what they felt was an "immoral war." The 1st Amendment was specifically included in the Constitution to protect political speech, and to prevent a "tyranny of the majority." The 1st Amendment protections would be meaningless if Congress could choose where and when citizen's rights may be diminished.

**For the United States:** A nation at war is justified in taking steps to insure the success of its effort to defend itself. The case involves congressional draft policy, not the 1st Amendment. Statements critical of the government cannot be tolerated in a crisis. The nation cannot allow an effort to deprive the armies of necessary soldiers. The actions and words of the Socialist party were a danger to the nation. The Espionage and Sedition acts, by contrast, were legitimate and appropriate in a time of war.

## Decision and Rationale

The Court's unanimous (9–0) decision was written by Justice Oliver Wendell Holmes. In it, the Court upheld Schenck's conviction, declaring the Espionage Act a reasonable and acceptable limitation on speech in time of war.

In the operative passage of the decision, Holmes wrote, "The most stringent protection of free speech would not protect a man in falsely shouting fire in a theatre and causing panic." Holmes argued that "The question in every case is whether the words used are used in such circumstances and are of such nature as to create a clear and present danger that they will bring about the substantive evils that Congress has a right to prevent."

In short, the Court held that reasonable limits can be imposed on the 1st Amendment's guarantee of free speech. No person may use free speech to place others in danger. "Protected political speech" was diminished in time of war.

The *Schenck* case stands as the first significant exploration of the limits of 1st Amendment free speech provisions by the Supreme Court. Its clarifications on the meaning of free speech have been modified, rewritten, and extended over the years. Flowing directly from this case, two schools of legal thought on the protections of the Bill of Rights emerged. One "absolutist" group felt that the Constitution meant to tolerate no interference by government with the people's freedoms, "absolutely none." More widely held was the "balancing doctrine," which suggested that the right of the people to be left alone by a government had to be "balanced" against "compelling public necessity."

© Prentice-Hall, Inc.

## Questions for Discussion

1. Does the "clear and present danger" test represent a reasonable means of balancing free speech and national security?
2. Did Schenck's actions present a real danger? Why or why not?

NAME ______________________ CLASS ______________ DATE ______________

# Close Up on the Supreme Court Landmark Cases
# *Powell* v. *Alabama,* 1932

## Historical Background

*The Alabama National Guard was called to guard the nine defendants after demonstrators threatened to attack the young men.*

By the 1930s, the reign of Jim Crow had reached its apex in the South. Segregation of the races remained the norm across the region—and, indeed, across the nation. Discrimination, exacerbated by the devastating effects of the Great Depression, was particularly harsh. A new Ku Klux Klan had arisen in the 1920s, marauding the nation with intimidation and terror. Social attitudes among white people in the South reflected a desire to keep the races "separate," to be sure, but far from "equal" according to the *Plessy* standard. Few African Americans voted, held public office, or even spoke publicly about abuses in the South.

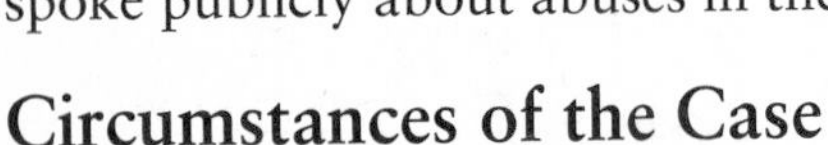

## Circumstances of the Case

Nine young African-American men hopped a ride aboard an empty freight train heading through Alabama. A group of young white men had also hopped aboard for transport through the State. A fight ensued between the groups, and all but one of the young white men were thrown from the train. Enraged, they sent a message ahead to the town of Scottsboro to report the incident. When the local sheriff and a posse of citizens stopped the train before it reached Scottsboro, two young white women testified that they had been sexually assaulted by the young African-American men on board the train.

All nine were taken into custody, and when word of the allegations spread angry crowds gathered around the jailhouse. Unable to restrain the demonstrators or guarantee the safety of the accused, the sheriff called for the Alabama National Guard.

Throughout the proceedings, none of the "Scottsboro" boys was allowed to contact their relatives, who lived out of State. On the day of the trial, an out-of-town attorney appeared for the defendants but announced that he could not formally represent them. The trial judge called on all the local lawyers present to assume responsibility for defending the nine young men, but only one agreed. The two lawyers had no opportunity to investigate the case or consult with their "clients." All nine youths were found guilty by four separate juries, despite testimony from doctors who said they found no evidence of rape upon examining the women. Eight of the nine men received the death penalty. The convictions were appealed through the State courts of Alabama, and failing there, went to the Supreme Court.

## Constitutional Issues

The question before the Court regarded the right to legal counsel guaranteed by the 6th Amendment, and how that right was applied to the States by the 14th Amendment. Must States provide counsel to citizens who cannot afford an attorney? Could a citizen be sentenced to death without benefit of counsel? Was the right to counsel so fundamental that the trial could not be fair without an attorney being provided? Was the right to counsel guaranteed in State trials by the 14th Amendment?

© Prentice Hall, Inc.

NAME ______________ CLASS ______________ DATE ______________



# *Powell* v. *Alabama*, 1932

## Arguments

**For Powell:** The Scottsboro trials were a travesty of justice—the accused having been railroaded through a discriminatory system. The young black men's right to counsel was so fundamental to criminal proceedings that any trial conducted without a defense attorney was not a fair trial at all. Alabama's conduct of the trial was unfair—a violation of a basic rule of decency and justice under the Constitution. Justice demanded that the death sentences be overturned and that new trials be ordered.

**For Alabama:** The right to legal counsel as stated in the 6th Amendment applies only to federal courts. Each State conducts its own criminal justice system, separate from federal authority, under the reserved powers of the Constitution. Alabama has its own bill of rights that recognizes the right of the accused to obtain counsel, but does not require the State to pay for attorneys to defend accused persons. The Supreme Court should not interfere with the internal operation of the State courts and it had never done so in 140 years. Moreover, an attorney defended the accused, but they were all convicted.

## Decision and Rationale

Justice Sutherland wrote the 7–2 majority opinion, overturning the convictions of the young black men and requiring that a new trial be held with the benefit of legal counsel appointed by the court. Sutherland wrote "No attempt was made to investigate.... Defendants were immediately hurried to trial...." The Court noted that "a defendant, charged with a serious crime, must not be stripped of his right to have sufficient time to advise with counsel and prepare his defense." To deny that, Sutherland wrote, "is not to proceed promptly in the calm spirit of regulated justice but to go forward with the haste of the mob."

The Court found that the right to counsel was one of the "'fundamental principles of liberty and justice which lie at the base of all our civil and political institutions'... We think the failure of the trial court to give [the young black men] reasonable time and opportunity to secure counsel was a clear denial of due process... '[T]here are certain immutable principles of justice which inhere in the very idea of free government which no member of the Union [no State] may disregard.'"

With this ruling, the Court set a precedent—under the Due Process Clause of the 14th Amendment, counsel must be guaranteed to everyone facing a possible death sentence, whether in State or federal court. The Scottsboro case was the beginning of an "incorporation" into State constitutions of fair trial rights guaranteed by the 6th Amendment. These rights were made applicable to the States by the 14th Amendment.

© Prentice-Hall, Inc.

## Questions for Discussion

1. According to Justice Sutherland, what does the right to counsel include?
2. What limitations remained on the right to counsel in the wake of the *Powell* decision?

NAME ______________________ CLASS ____________ DATE ____________

Close Up on the Supreme Court Landmark Cases

# *Brown* v. *Board of Education of Topeka*, 1954

## Historical Background

Perhaps no other case decided by the Court in the 20th century has had so profound an effect on the social fabric of America as *Brown* v. *Board of Education of Topeka*. By the end of World War II, dramatic changes in American race relations were already underway. The integration of labor unions in the 1930s under the eye of the Fair Employment Practices Commission and the desegregation of the armed forces by President Truman in 1948 marked major steps toward racial integration.

The legal framework on which segregation rested—formally established in 1896 by the Court's *Plessy* v. *Ferguson* decision—was itself being dismantled. Challenged repeatedly by the National Association for the Advancement of Colored People (NAACP), the doctrine of "separate but equal" was beginning to crack. Beginning in 1938, the Supreme Court had, in a number of cases, struck down laws where segregated facilities proved to be "demonstrably unequal." The Court ordered the law schools at the University of Missouri and the University of Texas to be integrated in *Missouri ex rel. Gaines* v. *Canada*, 1938, and *Sweatt* v. *Painter*, 1950. Neither case had made the frontal assault needed to overturn the Plessy standard. However, the 1950s brought a new wave of challenges to official segregation by the NAACP and other groups.

## Circumstances of the Case

Linda Brown, an eight-year-old African-American girl, had been denied permission to attend an elementary school only five blocks from her home in Topeka, Kansas. School officials refused to register her at the nearby school, assigning her instead to a school for nonwhite students some 21 blocks from her home. Separate elementary schools for whites and nonwhites were maintained by the Board of Education in Topeka. Linda Brown's parents filed a lawsuit to force the schools to admit her to the nearby, but segregated, school for white students.

## Constitutional Issues

The central question addressed to the Court involved the Equal Protection Clause of the 14th Amendment. "Does segregation of children in public schools solely on the basis of race, even though the physical facilities and other 'tangible' factors may be equal, deprive the children...of equal educational opportunities?" In short, the Court was asked to determine whether the segregation of schools was at all constitutional.

## Arguments

**For Linda Brown:** Led by Thurgood Marshall, an NAACP litigator who would be appointed to the Court in 1967, Brown's attorneys argued that the operation of separate schools, based on race, was harmful to African-American children. Extensive testimony was provided to support the contention that legal segregation resulted in both fundamentally unequal education and low self-esteem among minority students. The Brown family lawyers argued that segregation by law implied that African Americans were inherently inferior to whites.

Close Up on the Supreme Court Landmark Cases

# *Brown* v. *Board of Education of Topeka*, 1954

For these reasons they asked the Court to strike down segregation under the law.

**For the Board of Education:** Attorneys for Topeka argued that the separate schools for nonwhites in Topeka were equal in every way, and were in complete conformity with the *Plessy* standard. Buildings, the courses of study offered, and the quality of teachers were completely comparable. In fact, because some federal funds for Native Americans only applied at the nonwhite schools, some programs for minority children were actually better than those offered at the schools for whites. They pointed to the *Plessy* decision of 1896 to support segregation and argued that they had in good faith created "equal facilities," even though races were segregated. Furthermore, they argued, discrimination by race did not harm children.

## Decision and Rationale

For a unanimous Court (9–0), Chief Justice Warren wrote in his first and probably most significant decision, "[S]egregation [in public education] is a denial of the equal protection of the laws." Accepting the arguments put forward by the plaintiffs, Warren declared: "To separate [some children] from others of similar age and qualifications solely because of their race generates a feeling of inferiority as to their status in the community that may affect their hearts and minds in a way unlikely ever to be undone."

The Court quoted the Kansas court, which had held that "Segregation of white and colored children in public schools has a detrimental effect upon the colored children. The impact is greater when it has the sanction of the law; for the policy of separating the races is usually interpreted as denoting the inferiority of the negro group. A sense of inferiority affects the motivation of a child to learn. Segregation with the sanction of law, therefore, has a tendency to [retard] the educational and mental development of negro children and to deprive them of some of the benefits they would receive in a racial[ly] integrated school...."

Summing up, Warren wrote: "We conclude that in the field of public education the doctrine of 'separate but equal' has no place. Separate educational facilities are inherently unequal.... segregation [in public education] is a denial of the equal protection of the laws."

The *Brown* decision did more than reverse the *Plessy* doctrine of "separate but equal." It reversed centuries of segregationist practice and thought in America. For that reason, the *Brown* decision is seen as a transforming event—the birth of a political and social revolution. In a later case called *Brown II* (Warren had suggested two decisions—the first dealing with the constitutionality of segregation and the second with the implementation of the decision), the Court directed an end to school segregation by race "with all deliberate speed." The *Brown* decision became the cornerstone of the social justice movement of the 1950s and 1960s. It finally brought the spirit of the 14th Amendment into practice, more than three-quarters of a century after that amendment had been passed.

© Prentice-Hall, Inc.

## Questions for Discussion

1. Why was it significant that Brown was a unanimous decision of the Supreme Court?
2. What was the strongest argument in Chief Justice Warren's majority opinion? Why?

NAME ______________________ CLASS ______________ DATE ______________

# Close Up on the Supreme Court Landmark Cases
# *Mapp* v. *Ohio*, 1961

## Historical Background

The Warren Court left an unprecedented legacy of judicial activism in the area of civil rights law as well as in the area of civil liberties—specifically, the rights of the accused as addressed in Amendments 4 through 8. In the period from 1961 to 1969, the Warren Court examined almost every aspect of the criminal justice system in the United States, using the 14th Amendment to extend constitutional protections to all courts in every State. This process became known as the "nationalization" of the Bill of Rights. During those years, cases concerning the right to legal counsel, confessions, searches, and the treatment of juvenile criminals all appeared on the Court's docket.

The Warren Court's revolution in the criminal justice system began with the case of *Mapp* v. *Ohio*, the first of several significant cases in which it re-evaluated the role of the 14th Amendment as it applied to State judicial systems.

*Police officers must have a judge sign a search warrant before searching a home.*

## Circumstances of the Case

On May 23, 1957, police officers in a Cleveland, Ohio suburb received information that a suspect in a bombing case, as well as some illegal betting equipment, might be found in the home of Dollree Mapp. Three officers went to the home and asked for permission to enter, but Mapp refused to admit them without a search warrant. Two officers left, and one remained. Three hours later, the two returned with several other officers. Brandishing a piece of paper, they broke in the door. Mapp asked to see the "warrant" and took it from an officer, putting it in her dress. The officers struggled with Mapp and took the piece of paper away from her. They handcuffed her for being "belligerent."

Police found neither the bombing suspect nor the betting equipment during their search, but they did discover some pornographic material in a suitcase by Mapp's bed. Mapp said that she had loaned the suitcase to a boarder at one time and that the contents were not her property. She was arrested, prosecuted, found guilty, and sentenced for possession of pornographic material. No search warrant was introduced as evidence at her trial.

## Constitutional Issues

The question before the Court involved 4th Amendment protection against "unreasonable searches and seizures" and the "nationalization" of the Bill of Rights under the 14th Amendment. Was the search of Mapp's home legal and the evidence admissible under State law and criminal procedure? If the State criminal procedure code did not exclude the evidence as having been illegally gained, did Ohio law fail to provide Mapp her 4th Amendment protection against "unreasonable searches and seizures"? *Weeks* v. *United States*, 1914, established the exclusionary rule barring the admission of illegally obtained evidence in federal courts. Should that rule be extended, making evidence gained by an illegal search inadmissible in State courts as well?

## Arguments

**For Mapp:** The police, who possessed no warrant to search Mapp's property, had acted

# *Mapp* v. *Ohio*, 1961

improperly by doing so. Any incriminating evidence found during the search should, therefore, be thrown out of court and her conviction overturned. If the 4th Amendment did not limit the prerogatives of police on the local and State level, local law enforcement would have a mandate to search wherever, whenever, and whomever they pleased. The exclusionary rule that applied in federal courts should also be applied to State court proceedings.

**For the State of Ohio:** Even if the search was made without proper authority, the State was not prevented from using the evidence seized because "the Fourteenth Amendment does not forbid the admission of evidence obtained by an unreasonable search and seizure." In other words, Ohio argued, the 14th Amendment does not guarantee 4th Amendment protections in the State courts. Furthermore, under the 10th Amendment, the States retain their right to operate a separate court system. The Bill of Rights only restricts and limits the actions of the National Government.

## Decision and Rationale

In a 6–3 decision, the Court overturned the conviction, and five justices found that the States were bound to exclude evidence seized in violation of the 4th Amendment. In the majority opinion, Justice Tom Clark declared: "We hold that all evidence obtained by searches and seizures in violation of the Constitution [is] inadmissible in a state court.... Were it otherwise...the assurance against unreasonable...searches and seizures would be [meaningless]."

Clark explained that "Only last year [*Elkins* v. *United States,* 1960] the Court...recognized that the purpose of the exclusionary rule 'is to deter—to compel respect for the constitutional guarantee in the only effectively available way—by removing the incentive to disregard it.'" The Court thus ensured that "in either sphere [State or federal]...no man is to be convicted on unconstitutional evidence." The 4th Amendment sets the standards for searches and seizures by law enforcement officials in the United States, the Court noted, and the 14th Amendment requires judges to uphold those standards in every State.

Evidence gained by an illegal search became inadmissible in State courts as a result of the decision. The 50-year development of the exclusionary rule for illegal evidence, begun in the *Weeks* case, 1914, and continued in *Elkins*, 1960, culminated with the decision reached in *Mapp,* 1961.

The "*Mapp* Rule" has since been modified by decisions of the Burger Court, including *Nix* v. *Williams*, 1984 (inevitable discovery rule), and *U.S.* v. *Leon*, 1984 ("good faith" exception), so the exclusionary rule is no longer as absolute as when first handed down in *Mapp*. Critics of the Warren Court charged that it "had gone too far in interfering with police work."

© Prentice-Hall, Inc.

## Questions for Discussion

1. Justice Harlan dissented from the majority decision in *Mapp*, urging that the Court use "judicial restraint" rather than judicial activism. What do you think these terms mean in regard to the role the Court should play in determining government's role in society? Which do you believe to be the better judicial philosophy?
2. What wording in the 14th Amendment gave the Court a basis for applying the 4th Amendment to a State court proceeding?
3. Should criminals be released from custody because of an error of procedure made by police officers? Why or why not? Explain the rationale for either case.

NAME ______________________ CLASS ____________ DATE ____________

Close Up on the Supreme Court Landmark Cases

# *Engel* v. *Vitale,* 1962

## Historical Background

After World War II, the United States experienced another period of intense concern about the spread of communism abroad and fear of subversion at home. The Federal Government enacted a program requiring all employees to take loyalty oaths, while U.S. Senator Joseph McCarthy claimed there were communist agents in government. Alleged "communist spies" were called forth to give testimony before a Senate subcommittee chaired by McCarthy. These hearings had the impact of sensational court dramas that filled the media, while the deployment of U.S. soldiers to fight communist aggression in Korea made the threat of communism at home all the more palpable. In this context, some States enacted a variety of programs to encourage patriotism, moral character, and other values of good citizenship. They also began challenging separation of church and state issues in hopes of providing students with strong moral and spiritual stamina. In this case, the Warren Court once again was to take up a controversial issue.

*Justice Hugo Black*

## Circumstances of the Case

In 1951 the New York State Board of Regents (the State board of education) approved a 22-word "nondenominational prayer" for recitation each morning in the public schools of New York. It read: "Almighty God, we acknowledge our dependence upon Thee, and we beg Thy blessings upon us, our parents, our teachers and our Country." The Regents believed that the prayer could be a useful tool for the development of character and good citizenship among the students of the State of New York. The prayer was offered to the school boards in the State for their use, and participation in the "prayer-exercise" was voluntary. In New Hyde Park, New York, the Union Free School District No. 9 directed the local principal to have the prayer "said aloud by each class in the presence of a teacher at the beginning of the school day."

The parents of ten pupils in the New Hyde Park schools objected to the prayer. They filed suit in a New York State court seeking a ban on the prayer, insisting that the use of this official prayer in the public schools was contrary to their own and their children's beliefs, religions, or religious practices. The State appeals court upheld the use of the prayer, "so long as the schools did not compel any pupil to join in the prayer over his or his parents' objection."

## Constitutional Issues

The question before the Court involved the Establishment Clause of the 1st Amendment. Did the Regents of New York violate the religious freedom of students by providing time during the school day for this particular prayer? Did the prayer itself represent an unconstitutional action—in effect, the establishment of a religious code—by a public agency? Did the Establishment Clause of the 1st Amendment prevent schools from engaging in "religious activity"? Was the "wall of separation" between church and state breached in this case?

© Prentice Hall, Inc.

NAME ______________________ CLASS ____________ DATE ____________



# *Engel* v. *Vitale,* 1962

## Arguments

**For Engel (the parents):** The separation of church and state requires that government stay out of the business of prescribing religious activities of any kind. The Regents' prayer quite simply and clearly violated the 1st Amendment and should, therefore, be barred from the schools.

**For the Regents of the State of New York:** The New York Regents did not establish a religion by providing a prayer for those who wanted to say it. Countless religious elements are associated with governments and officials, reflecting the religious heritage of the nation. New York acted properly and constitutionally in providing an optional, nonsectarian prayer. It would be an intrusion into State matters for the Supreme Court to strike down the right of the Regents to compose the prayer and encourage its recitation.

## Decision and Rationale

The Court found the New York Regents' prayer to be unconstitutional. Justice Hugo Black wrote the opinion for the 6–1 majority: "We think that by using its public school system to encourage recitation of the Regents' Prayer, the State of New York has adopted a practice wholly inconsistent with the Establishment Clause. There can, of course, be no doubt that New York's program of daily classroom invocation of God's blessings...in the Regents' Prayer is a religious activity..."

Black further explained that "When the power, prestige and financial support of government is placed behind a particular religious belief, the indirect coercive pressure upon religious minorities to conform to the prevailing officially approved religion is plain.... The Establishment Clause thus stands as an expression of principle on the part of the Founders of our Constitution that religion is too personal, too sacred, too holy, to permit its 'unhallowed perversion' by a civil magistrate."

To support the Court's finding, Black referred to the following ideas of the Framers: "To those who may subscribe to the view that because the Regents' official prayer is so brief and general [it] can be no danger to religious freedom..., it may be appropriate to say in the words of James Madison, the author of the First Amendment:... 'Who does not see that the same authority which can establish Christianity, in exclusion of all other Religions, may establish with the same ease any particular sect of Christians, in exclusion of all other Sects?'"

The Court's decision was not, Black pointed out, antireligious. It sought, rather, only to affirm the separation between church and state. "It is neither sacrilegious nor antireligious to say that each separate government in this country should stay out of the business of writing or sanctioning official prayers..." Thereafter, State governments could not "prescribe by law any particular form of prayer which is to be used as an official prayer in carrying on any program of governmentally sponsored religious activity."

© Prentice-Hall, Inc.

## Questions for Discussion

1. The First Amendment states: "Congress shall make no law respecting an establishment of religion, or prohibiting the free exercise thereof." Does this amendment provide for a separation of church and state?

2. Does the Court's decision in *Engel* take both the Establishment and Free Exercise Clauses into account? Is Black correct in claiming that the Court's opinion is not anti-religious?

NAME ______ CLASS ______ DATE ______

# Close Up on the Supreme Court Landmark Cases
# *Miranda* v. *Arizona*, 1966

## Historical Background

With its decisions in the cases of *Mapp* v. *Ohio*, 1961, *Gideon* v. *Wainwright*, 1963, and *Escobedo* v. *Illinois*, 1964, the Warren Court handed down the bases of what it called the "fundamentals of fairness" standard. At both the State and federal level, the Court sent a clear signal to law enforcement and criminal justice officials. Convictions not made in conformity with the "fairness" standard would likely be overturned. Constitutional guarantees of due process for the accused had to be upheld.

*Ernesto Miranda (right) leaving the courtroom with his attorney.*

The Court heard a number of similar cases at the same time that it heard *Miranda*, but since this case was listed first on the docket, we have come to know the Court's collective judgment by this name. The *Miranda* decision distilled the several "fundamental fairness" standards into one succinct statement of the due process rights of the accused. Thanks to television police shows, the Miranda warning has become a statement of a citizen's rights familiar to many Americans.

## Circumstances of the Case

A kidnapping and sexual assault occurred in Phoenix, Arizona, in March 1963. On March 13 Ernesto Miranda, 23, was arrested in his home, taken to the police station, identified by the victim, and taken into an interrogation room. Miranda was not told of his rights to counsel prior to questioning. Two hours later, investigators emerged from the room with a written confession signed by Miranda. It included a typed disclaimer, also signed by Miranda, stating that he had "full knowledge of my legal rights, understanding any statement I make may be used against me," and that he had knowingly waived those rights.

Two weeks later at a preliminary hearing, Miranda again was denied counsel. At his trial he did have a lawyer, whose objections to the use of Miranda's signed confession as evidence were overruled. Miranda was convicted of kidnapping and rape, and received a 20-year sentence.

## Constitutional Issues

Was a confession an admissible document in a court of law if it was obtained without warnings against self-incrimination and without legal counsel—rights guaranteed to all persons by the 5th and 6th amendments? With whom does the burden of proof rest for determining whether a defendant has legally "waived" his or her rights? What is the standard for judging whether "voluntary confessions" should be deemed admissible? When should an attorney be appointed for a person if he or she cannot afford one?

## Arguments

**For Miranda:** The police clearly violated Miranda's 5th Amendment right to remain silent, and his 6th Amendment right to legal counsel. Arizona ignored both the *Escobedo* rule (evidence obtained from an illegally obtained confession is inadmissible in court) and the *Gideon* rule (all felony defendants have the right to an attorney) in prosecuting Miranda. His confession was illegally obtained and should be thrown out. His conviction was faulty, and he deserved a new trial.

© Prentice Hall, Inc.

Close Up on the Supreme Court Landmark Cases

# *Miranda* v. *Arizona*, 1966

**For Arizona:** Ernesto Miranda was no stranger to police procedures. He negotiated with police officers with intelligence and understanding. He signed the confession willingly. The prosecution was proper, his conviction was based on Arizona law, and his imprisonment was just. The Supreme Court should uphold his conviction and should not further cripple the work of police.

## Decision and Rationale

By a 5–4 margin, the Court voted to overturn Miranda's conviction. Writing for the majority, Chief Justice Warren declared that the burden is upon the State to demonstrate that "procedural safeguards effective to secure the privilege against self-incrimination" are followed. "The current practice of 'incommunicado' [unable to communicate with the world] interrogation is at odds with one of our Nation's most cherished principles—that the individual may not be compelled to incriminate himself."

Warren then summarized the case, measuring it against the "fundamental fairness" standards the Court had established. "[I]t is clear," he wrote, "that Miranda was not in any way apprised of his right to consult with an attorney and to have one present during the interrogation, nor was his right not to be compelled to incriminate himself effectively protected in any other manner. Without these warnings [his] statements were inadmissible. The mere fact that he signed a statement which contained a typed-in clause stating that he had 'full knowledge' of his 'legal rights' does not approach the knowing and intelligent waiver required to relinquish constitutional rights."

Turning to the standard for a valid waiver of rights, Warren wrote: "[A] valid waiver will not be presumed simply from the silence of the accused after warnings are given or simply from the fact that a confession was in fact eventually obtained.... Moreover, any evidence that the accused was threatened, tricked or cajoled into a waiver will, of course, show that the defendant did not voluntarily waive his privilege."

Warren then spelled out the rights of the accused and the responsibilities of the police. Police must warn a suspect "prior to any questioning that he has the right to remain silent, that anything he says can be used against him in a court of law, that he has the right to the presence of an attorney, and that if he cannot afford an attorney one will be appointed for him prior to any questioning if he so desires."

The creation of the Miranda Warning put on the shoulders of the police the burden of informing citizens subject to questioning in a criminal investigation of their rights to "due process." Ernesto Miranda, retracting his confession, was tried again by the State of Arizona, found guilty, and sent to prison. His retrial, based on a prisoner's successful appeal, did not constitute "double jeopardy."

© Prentice-Hall, Inc.

## Questions for Discussion

1. Why is it essential that a person be given the right to counsel during police interrogation as well as during the trial?
2. Opponents of the Miranda decision argue that procedural safeguards imposed on police as a result of this ruling undermine criminal investigations. Should such concerns outweigh protection of individual rights?

NAME ______________________ CLASS ______________ DATE ______________

Close Up on the Supreme Court Landmark Cases

# *New York Times Co.* v. *United States*, 1971

## Historical Background

Over the years the Supreme Court has disagreed on the limits that can be placed on the 1st Amendment guarantees of freedom of speech and press. In 1971, the Court faced these issues again in a case brought by the *New York Times*. The newspaper had obtained a copy of documents known as "The Pentagon Papers"— an internal Defense Department report that detailed government deception with regard to the Vietnam War. The Pentagon Papers surfaced at a time when the American people were deeply divided on the question of United States involvement in the war. The *New York Times* fought for the right to publish the papers under the umbrella of the 1st Amendment.

## Circumstances of the Case

The Pentagon Papers, officially known as "History of U.S. Decision-Making Process on Viet Nam Policy," were illegally copied and then leaked to the press. The *New York Times* and the *Washington Post* had obtained the documents. Acting at the Government's request, the United States district court in New York issued a temporary injunction—a court order—that directed the *New York Times* not to publish the documents. The Government claimed that the publication of the papers would endanger the security of the United States. The *New York Times* appealed the order to the United States Supreme Court, arguing that prior restraint—preventing publication—violated the 1st Amendment.

## Constitutional Issues

Are the freedoms provided by the 1st Amendment absolute? Did the threat to national security outweigh the freedom of press guaranteed by the 1st Amendment? Did the publication of the Pentagon Papers in fact pose a threat to national security?

## Arguments

**For the *New York Times*:** The 1st Amendment's guarantee of freedom of the press protects the newspaper in the publication of these documents. One of the few restraints on executive power in matters of national defense is a knowledgeable population. The press must be free to inform the American people. In addition, the Government has failed to show that publication of the Pentagon Papers would endanger national security.

**For the United States:** The 1st Amendment does not guarantee an absolute freedom of the press, especially when the nation's security is involved. The Court must strike a balance between the fundamentally important right to a free press and the equally important duty of the Government to protect the nation. Allowing the publication of these documents would establish a dangerous precedent for future cases involving national security.

*American Paratroopers drop into a grass field in Phan Rang, Vietnam, during the Vietnam War.*

© Prentice-Hall, Inc.

NAME ______________________ CLASS ______________ DATE ______________

Close Up on the Supreme Court Landmark Cases

# *New York Times Co.* v. *United States*, 1971

## Decision and Rationale

By a 6–3 decision, the Court ruled in favor of the *New York Times*. In the judgment, the Court cited a prevailing precedent, noting: "Any system of prior restraints of expression comes to this Court bearing a heavy presumption against its constitutional validity." In other words, the Court would not be favorably disposed to stifling the press on the order of the government.

*Daniel Ellsberg, the Defense Department analyst who "leaked" The Pentagon Papers, speaking to reporters about his trial.*

Justices Hugo Black and William Douglas, members of the majority, held that the 1st Amendment is absolute. Justice Black called it "unfortunate" in his view "that some of my Brethren [fellow justices] are apparently willing to hold that the publication of news may sometimes be enjoined. Such a holding," he wrote, "would make a shambles of the First Amendment."

Justice Byron White, joined by Justice Potter Stewart, believed that while there are situations in which the 1st Amendment may be abridged, they had to "concur in today's judgments, but only because of the concededly extraordinary protection against prior restraints enjoyed by the press under our constitutional system." Although the justices thought that the *New York Times* had probably gone too far in publishing the Pentagon Papers, they found nothing in the law to prevent the newspaper from doing so.

Deferring to responsibilities of the Executive, Chief Justice Warren Burger dissented. Given those vast responsibilities, Burger noted, the Executive also had to be given broader authority. "In these cases, the imperative of a free and unfettered press comes into collision with another imperative, the effective functioning of a complex modern government and specifically the effective exercise of certain constitutional powers of the Executive," Burger wrote. "Only those who view the First Amendment as an absolute in all circumstances—a view I respect, but reject—can find such cases as these to be simple or easy."

The decision reinforced the Court's stance against prior restraint and has often been noted in subsequent prior restraint cases. In the spring of 2000, a Texas district court judge ordered the Associated Press (AP) not to publish a story about a state-guaranteed loan to a Texas shrimp farm. Lawyers for the AP cited the *New York Times* case in their argument. The judge lifted the order after two days of hearings.

© Prentice-Hall, Inc.

## Questions for Discussion

1. In terms of freedom of the press, what is the difference between prior restraint and punishment after the fact?
2. Do you think that prior restraint should disallowed under all circumstances? If not, under what circumstances do you think it should be allowed.

NAME ____________________ CLASS ____________ DATE ____________

# Close Up on the Supreme Court Landmark Cases
# *Roe* v. *Wade*, 1973

## Historical Background

Since the Supreme Court's decision in *Roe* v. *Wade*, the legal, moral, and political controversy surrounding the abortion issue has polarized the American public. Two camps—one hailing *Roe* as a victory for "choice," the other arguing that the decision deprives the unborn child of its "right to life"—squared off in the wake of the Court's decision. Their protracted political battle continues today. The deep political divisions that the case created, or revealed, reflect not only conflicting social and moral views, but conflicting views of the law as well. The case pitted two accepted doctrines against one another—the individual's "right to privacy" and the "compelling and overriding interest" of a State. *Roe* v. *Wade* sought an extension of the "right to privacy," which the Court explicitly recognized for the first time in the case *Griswold* v. *Connecticut*, 1965. In that case, family counselors in Connecticut challenged a State law forbidding the use of "any drug, medicinal article or instrument for the purpose of preventing conception." In *Griswold*, the Court decided that there was a "right of privacy" implied by the Bill of Rights. It ruled that the 1st, 3rd, 4th, 5th, 9th, and 14th Amendments together create a right of "marital privacy."

## Circumstances of the Case

In Texas, State law prohibited the termination of a pregnancy by artificial means (surgery) except when the life of the mother was in danger. The statute was construed as a "nearly complete ban on abortion." A Texas woman, claiming privacy as a "fundamental right," challenged the Texas statute. In 1971 the case was argued before the Supreme Court. In 1972 it was argued again. *Roe* and a companion case from Georgia, *Doe* v. *Bolton*, were the first cases to test, in the Court, the newly recognized "right of privacy" against the "compelling interest" of the States to regulate abortions.

## Constitutional Issues

This case involved the right of privacy as implied by Amendments 1, 3, 4, 5, 9, and 14 versus the police power of the States. Did States have a compelling and overriding interest in regulating the health, safety, and morals of the community? Was there an area of personal, marital, familial, and sexual privacy protected by the Bill of Rights? Was the Texas law an unreasonable invasion of privacy, or was it a reasonable exercise of the police power? Were women permitted to terminate pregnancies "at will," or were fetuses "persons" with rights to be protected by the State?

## Arguments

**For Roe:** Under the Bill of Rights, a woman has the right to terminate her pregnancy. It is

*Americans on both sides of the abortion issue continue to fight for their beliefs today.*

© Prentice-Hall, Inc.

improper for a State to deny individuals the personal, marital, familial, and sexual right to privacy. Moreover, in no case in its history has the Court declared that a fetus—a developing infant in the womb—is a person. Therefore, the fetus cannot be said to have any legal "right to life." Because it is unduly intrusive, the Texas law is unconstitutional and should be overturned.

**For Wade:** The State has a duty to protect prenatal life. Life is present at the moment of conception. The unborn are people, and as such are entitled to protection under the Constitution. The Texas law is a valid exercise of police powers reserved to the States in order to protect the health and safety of citizens, including the unborn. The law is constitutional and should be upheld.

## Decision and Rationale

By a vote of 7–2, with Justices White and Rehnquist in dissent, the Court agreed with Roe and upheld her right to terminate a pregnancy in the first trimester (90 days). The Court observed that Section 1 of the 14th Amendment contained three references to "person." In his majority opinion, Justice Blackmun noted that, for nearly all such references in the Constitution, "use of the word is such that it has application only postnatally. None indicates, with any assurance, that it has any possible prenatal application."

Blackmun's opinion carefully steered between the right to privacy and the question of compelling State interest. On the first point, he wrote, the majority of the justices "do not agree" with Texas that the State "may override the rights of the pregnant woman that are at stake." On the other hand, the State does have an "important and legitimate interest in protecting the potentiality of human life" and in protecting the mother's health. Blackmun's decision revolved around the development of the fetus during pregnancy. He held that during the first trimester, or three months, of a pregnancy, the woman in consultation with her physician had an unrestricted right to an abortion. During the second trimester, States could regulate abortion to protect a woman's health. Finally, during the third trimester, the State's interest in protecting the potential life of the fetus was sufficient to justify severe restrictions.

Approaching the matter of when life begins, Blackmun was clearly hesitant to commit the Court to any position.

Controversial when announced, the *Roe* decision remains at the center of the legal controversy over the right to privacy versus the rights of the unborn. In *Planned Parenthood of Southeastern Pennsylvania* v. *Casey*, 1992, the Court reaffirmed *Roe's* central holding but abandoned its trimester structure. The Court permitted States to require informed consent, a 24-hour waiting period, and/or parental notification, but held that States may not place an "undue burden"on a woman's right to an abortion.

© Prentice-Hall, Inc.

## Questions for Discussion

1. Is a right to privacy guaranteed by the Constitution? If so, what are the sources of that right? In what circumstances should that right be protected?
2. States have a "police power" that allows governments to establish and enforce regulations relating to the health, safety, welfare and morals of the community. Should abortion fall under the "police power" traditionally exercised by the state? Why or why not?

NAME ______________ CLASS ______________ DATE ______________

Close Up on the Supreme Court Landmark Cases

# *United States* v. *Nixon*, 1974

## Historical Background

The early 1970s was a time of growing distrust in the National Government. The Pentagon Papers exposed the intentional deception of the American people about Vietnam. Americans were shocked when the National Guard opened fire at a Kent State University protest following President Nixon's authorization for the United States to attack Cambodia. Four students were killed. Nixon would soon add more fuel to the fire, attempting to cover up illegal actions by himself and his administration.

## Circumstances of the Case

In June 1972, five men armed with cameras and bugging equipment were arrested inside the Democratic National Committee's offices in the Watergate complex in Washington, D.C. Police soon discovered that the burglars worked, directly or indirectly, for the Committee to Re-Elect the President. President Nixon and leaders of his campaign denied any connection with the incident.

The five men were convicted of burglary, along with E. Howard Hunt, Jr., a former Nixon aide, and G. Gordon Liddy, a lawyer for the Committee to Re-elect the President. Shortly afterward, the presiding judge received a letter from one of the convicted men. It spoke of payoffs to the burglars in return for their silence—the men had perjured themselves to protect others involved in the break-in.

In 1973, a Senate select committee began an investigation, and it became clear that top members of the Nixon administration were involved in a cover-up of the break-in and several other illegal actions. It was also discovered that Nixon had installed a taping system that automatically recorded all of his conversations with his advisors. A special prosecutor appointed to probe the Watergate scandal subpoenaed the tapes. Nixon refused to release them, claiming they were protected under executive privilege. Nixon eventually released some of the tapes, but portions of them had been erased. Finally, another special prosecutor asked the United States Supreme Court to compel Nixon to release all of the tapes in their entirety.

## Constitutional Issues

Does the separation of powers created by the Constitution provide the President with an

*Richard Nixon boards a helicopter on the day of his resignation from the presidency. Nixon said that although he was inclined to stay and fight, he thought his resignation would be better for the country.*

© Prentice-Hall, Inc.

NAME ______________________ CLASS ______________ DATE ______________



# ***United States* v. *Nixon*, 1974**

absolute power to withhold information from other branches of government? If the power is not absolute, should President Nixon be able to claim executive privilege under the aforementioned circumstances? Does the separation of powers allow for the settlement of this dispute to reside in the executive branch or should it be settled by the judicial branch? Does the claim of executive privilege damage the precedent set by the 5th Amendment, which ensures due process?

## Arguments

**For the United States:** The President's power to claim executive privilege is not an absolute one. Executive privilege may not be invoked to deny the courts access to evidence needed in a criminal proceeding. This is a dispute that can properly be heard in the federal courts.

**For President Nixon:** The constitutional scheme of separation of powers grants to the President the privilege of withholding information from the other branches of government. Furthermore, this power is absolute, and it is vital where high-level communications are involved. In addition, this dispute should be resolved within the executive branch, not by the courts.

## Decision and Rationale

The Court ruled unanimously that President Richard Nixon had to surrender the tapes. Chief Justice Warren Burger delivered the opinion of the Court. Burger wrote, "The impediment that an absolute, unqualified [executive] privilege would place in the way of the primary constitutional duty of the Judicial Branch to do justice in criminal prosecutions would plainly conflict with the function of the courts under Art[icle] III."

Burger then turned his attention to the damage that a privilege of confidentiality would cause to citizens' constitutional rights: "The right to the production of all evidence at a criminal trial similarly has constitutional dimensions. The Sixth Amendment explicitly confers upon every defendant in a criminal trial the right 'to be confronted with the witnesses against him' and 'to have compulsory process for obtaining witnesses in his favor.' Moreover, the Fifth Amendment also guarantees that no person shall be deprived of liberty without due process. It is the manifest duty of the courts to vindicate those guarantees, and to accomplish that it is essential that all relevant and admissible evidence be produced." The Court made it clear that the President could not withhold evidence from an ongoing criminal prosecution of another person simply because he was the President.

Several days before, the House Judiciary Committee had approved three articles of impeachment. On August 9, 1974, Nixon became the first President in U.S. history to resign from the presidency. He did so in order to avoid going through the likely prospect of being impeached by the full House of Representatives and convicted by the Senate.

## Questions for Discussion

1. Do you think the outcome of this case would have been the same if President Nixon had claimed national security needs rather than executive privilege? Why or why not?
2. Under what circumstances do you think executive privilege can be legitimately claimed?
3. By taping conversations in the Oval Office, was President Nixon violating the rights of the people he taped? If so, what rights were violated?

© Prentice Hall, Inc.

Close Up on the Supreme Court Landmark Cases

# *New Jersey* v. *T.L.O.*, 1985

## Historical Background

The Supreme Court has a long history of upholding citizens' protections against unreasonable searches and seizures—a right guaranteed by the 4th Amendment. In *Weeks* v. *United States*, 1914, the Court ruled that evidence obtained by police illegally is not admissible in federal court—a practice known as the exclusionary rule. The Court decided that such evidence is also inadmissible in State courts in *Mapp* v. *Ohio*, 1961. The Supreme Court extended 4th Amendment protections to include not only tangible property, but also intangible items obtained without a warrant, such as phone conversations (*Katz* v. *United States*, 1967). However, the 4th Amendment does not apply to such items as garbage placed on a curb (*California* v. *Greenwood*, 1988).

But does the 4th Amendment clause apply to students? In 1985, a New Jersey high school student was arrested as a result of a search and seizure conducted by her assistant vice-principal. The constitutionality of the search was questioned and ultimately the Supreme Court faced the task of establishing parameters for searches and seizures in schools.

*Metal detectors are now used in many schools across the country, as in this Philadelphia, Pennsylvania high school.*

## Circumstances of the Case

In 1980, a teacher at Piscataway High School in Middlesex County, New Jersey, found T.L.O. and another girl smoking in a restroom—a place that was by school rule a nonsmoking area. The two girls were taken to the principal's office where T.L.O.'s companion admitted that she had been smoking in the restroom. T.L.O. denied smoking there. She denied that she smoked at all. An assistant vice-principal demanded to see T.L.O.'s purse. Searching through it he found a pack of cigarettes. He also found rolling papers, a pipe, marijuana, a large wad of dollar bills, and two letters that indicated that T.L.O. was involved in marijuana dealing at the high school.

T.L.O. was taken to the police station where she confessed that she had sold marijuana at the school. A juvenile court sentenced her to a year's probation. The State Supreme Court overturned the decision, stating that T.L.O.'s 4th Amendment rights had been violated. The State of New Jersey asked that the Supreme Court hear its appeal.

## Constitutional Issues

Do students in school have the same rights under the 4th Amendment as adults? Does "probable cause" have to be established for the search of a student in school, or is "reasonable cause" enough?

## Arguments

**For New Jersey:** School officials act for the parents of students. Like parents, they do not need a warrant to make searches or seize evidence. School officials also must have broad powers to control student conduct, including the powers of search and seizure. T.L.O.'s behavior furnished a reasonable basis for the search of her purse; therefore, the exclusionary rule does not apply.

**For T.L.O:** Public school officials are employees of the State, not representatives of parents. They do not have the right to act as parents. Because school officials are employees of the State, they are obligated to respect every stu-

© Prentice-Hall, Inc.

# *New Jersey* v. *T.L.O.*, 1985

dent's rights, including his or her right to privacy. The search of T.L.O.'s purse and the seizure of its contents were unreasonable acts, which led to her confession; therefore, the exclusionary rule applies.

## Decision and Rationale

The Court ruled by a margin of 6–3 in favor of New Jersey. Justice Byron White wrote the Court's opinion. White recognized that students in public schools have a constitutional right to privacy under the 4th Amendment and that school officials are bound by constitutional restrictions. But the opinion also stated that the rights of children and adolescents are not the same as those of adults and that school officials have a responsibility to maintain the discipline necessary for education. "The school setting," White wrote, "...requires some modification of the level of suspicion of illicit activity needed to justify a search." The rights of students must be balanced against the needs of the school setting.

Usually, White noted, "probable cause" that a legal violation has occurred must exist. But White agreed with a lower court finding that a "school official may properly conduct a search of a student's person if the official has a reasonable suspicion that a crime has been...committed, or reasonable cause to believe that the search is necessary to maintain school discipline...." In other words, in a school, a search could be reasonable under the 4th Amendment without probable cause, so long as it was supported by reasonable suspicion or reasonable cause. The assistant vice-principal's search was considered reasonable under this definition.

In his partial dissent, Justice William Brennan wrote that the "decision sanctions school officials to conduct full scale searches on a 'reasonableness' standard whose only definite content is that it is not the same test as the 'probable cause' standard found in the text of the Fourth Amendment." In other words, he was concerned that the unclear distinction between "probable" and "reasonable" cause would discourage teachers from carrying out permissible searches.

The Court's decision would serve as a precedent in cases to come. In *Bethel School District* v. *Fraser*, 1986, the Court upheld school disciplinary action taken against a student who delivered a sexually explicit speech nominating a fellow student for elective office. Although the case dealt with 1st Amendment protections rather than those of the 4th Amendment, the Court based the decision on the following: "In *New Jersey* v. *T.L.O.* (1985)... we reaffirmed that the constitutional rights of students in public school are not automatically coextensive with the rights of adults in other settings."

In the 1990s, the *T.L.O.* decision was used a number of times in Supreme Court cases to allow the use of metal detectors and protective searches in school. The Court has likened such searches to airport scanning and highway checkpoints for drunk drivers.

© Prentice-Hall, Inc.

## Questions for Discussion

1. Does White's standard find the right balance between a student's right to privacy and a school's concern with discipline? Why or why not?
2. Should warrantless searches be limited to cases involving violent, unlawful, or seriously disruptive conduct?

NAME ______ CLASS ______ DATE ______

Close Up on the Supreme Court Landmark Cases

# *Cruzan* v. *Director, Missouri Dept. of Health,* 1990

## Historical Background

At the time of the *Cruzan* case, about 10,000 Americans were living in a persistent, comatose state. No one was sure who, if anyone, had the authority to end these people's lives. Healthy older people became depressed by the possibility of living in such a condition during the last years of their lives. Under such circumstances, does a person have a personal, private right to choose when to end his or her life? Does this right override any compelling State interest in the prevention of suicide?

## Circumstances of the Case

Twenty-five year-old Nancy Cruzan was in an automobile accident in 1983. Massive injuries resulted in her falling into an unconscious state, unresponsive to outside stimulation. She was placed on life-support equipment and was fed intravenously. After emerging from a three-week long coma, Nancy remained in a "persistent vegetative state," a condition in which an unconscious person displays motor reflexes but exhibits no indications of significant cognitive function. Although doctors felt that she could endure many more years in her present condition—that is, with her life functions carried out by machine support-her own doctor said she had no chance of recovery.

Five years after the accident and facing a hopeless prognosis, Nancy's parents asked that their daughter's feeding tubes be disconnected. By then, most of the annual cost for her hospitalization was being paid by the State of Missouri. The catastrophic cost of Nancy's care had exhausted the family's resources.

A Missouri district court granted the request of the Cruzan family, but the director of the Missouri Department of Health took the case on appeal to the Missouri Supreme Court. Missouri insisted on a high standard of proof of Cruzan's wish to die. The State argued that Cruzan's casual statement before the accident that she would not want to live as a "vegetable" was not "clear and convincing evidence" that she would want to be taken off the life-support equipment. The Missouri Supreme Court refused to authorize the termination of artificial feeding for Nancy. Life support was continued and the Cruzans appealed to the Supreme Court.

*The Cruzan family speaks to reporters about the case.*

## Constitutional Issues

Is there a "family right of sovereignty" that overrides the State's interest in preserving life? Would Nancy Cruzan, presently unable to make decisions for herself, choose to live in this condition? Nancy did not leave specific instructions to terminate life support if she were ever in a persistent, comatose state. Who, then, should decide to withhold medical treatment? The family? A doctor? A court?

## Arguments

**For the Cruzan Family:** The decision of the Missouri Supreme Court was not wise. It considered the general ramifications of the decision on matters such as suicide and abortion, rather than deciding the Cruzan case on its own merits. It neglected to consider the pain and suffering of Nancy Cruzan and her family. Moreover, the enormous cost to the State for Nancy Cruzan's care could be better spent on medical procedures for children facing death. Family and friends of severely injured people should be able to consult with medical-care providers and make a decision about the patient's continued life support.

Close Up on the Supreme Court Landmark Cases

# *Cruzan* v. *Director, Missouri Dept. of Health,* 1990

**For the State of Missouri:** The State of Missouri has an unqualified interest in the preservation of life. Regardless of the condition of the patient, the overt action of removing feeding tubes constitutes murder under Missouri law. To permit any life-threatening action by a medical caregiver is to violate Missouri criminal law. The action of the Missouri Supreme Court, in staying the order of the district court, was wise and appropriate.

## Decision and Rationale

When the Court considered the problems of death and medical technology in this case, the vote was 5–4 to uphold Missouri's stand. The Court felt that the *Cruzan* case was best explored in the area of "liberty" rather than "privacy." The Supreme Court upheld the authority of States to demand "clear and convincing" evidence of the injured person's wishes.

The Court ruled that the State of Missouri could prohibit the Cruzan family from removing feeding tubes from Nancy because there was no clear evidence that she would have wanted medical treatment stopped. The majority's main problem was that of trust in the judgment of close family members. Chief Justice Rehnquist noted that "Close family members may have a strong feeling—a feeling not at all ignoble or unworthy, but not entirely disinterested, either—that they do not wish to witness the continuation of the life of a loved one which they regard as hopeless." The decision of the Court in *Cruzan* indicated the Court's primary concern with the preservation of life, even at the expense of "family sovereignty."

Justice Brennan dissented, with Justices Marshall and Blackmun joining. They also cited the idea of liberty in their argument, but stated that Cruzan's entitlement to liberty—in this case, the liberty to refuse medical treatment—outweighed any interests of the State. Justice Stevens' dissent also argued that the State was usurping Cruzan's rights. He wrote: "The meaning and completion of her life should be controlled by persons who have her best interests at heart—not by a state legislature concerned only with the 'preservation of human life.'" Since the *Cruzan* decision, which upheld the prerogative of States to demand "clear and convincing evidence," there has been a great interest in "living wills." In these documents, signed before witnesses, citizens may record a legal statement indicating their wishes should they become catastrophically injured. A living will may prohibit prolonged tube feeding and mechanical respiration, or resuscitation—restarting the heart by artificial means. In many States, a legal order called a "power of attorney" allows a friend or relative to speak on a person's behalf when a traumatic injury occurs.

After the Court upheld the right of Missouri to demand "clear and convincing evidence," a new hearing was held before a Missouri court to determine Nancy Cruzan's fate. After hearing testimony, a State judge authorized the disconnecting of the feeding tubes. Nancy Cruzan died several days later.

© Prentice-Hall, Inc.

## Questions for Discussion

1. Compare and contrast the issues raised in this case with those raised in *Roe* v. *Wade*. How do you account for the differences in the Court's treatment of these issues? Are the differences valid?

2. The central question of the case involves determining what is "clear and convincing evidence" of a person's wish to die. How would you define the concept? Should next of kin and medical-care providers be empowered to make that decision?

# Answer Key

## Extension Activities

**Chapter 1, p. 2**

**1.** Arguments for allowing federal court review include (1) the issue does not involve political judgments that would prevent judicial review; and (2) citizens have the right to use the courts to ensure the full constitutional value of their right to vote. One argument against federal court review is that the Court should respect the legislature's chosen apportionment, which is made with citizens' best interests in mind. Some students will find those arguments for federal court review most convincing while others will be more convinced by the argument against it. **2.** Some students might think the number of senators per State contradicts the Court's decision in *Baker* v. *Carr* because States as lightly populated as Rhode Island have as many senators representing them as heavily populated States, such as Texas. Others might think it does not contradict this case's decision because the Senate is only one house of Congress. In the other house, the House of Representatives, the number of members from each State is relative to the State's population.

**Chapter 2, p. 3**

**1.** Brennan thought that the Court's role is to decide what is constitutional, not what is popular. The First Amendment protects communications that may be unpopular. **2.** Students who agree with the Court might argue that the wearing of the flag is a protected expression of an idea. Opponents might say that it is as offensive as flag-burning and should not be allowed. Others might say that it is less offensive then burning so it should not be banned.

**Chapter 3, p. 4**

**1.** Justice Powell stated that the amendment applied only to convicted criminals. Justice White responded that the amendment does not include the word "criminal" so it is not explicitly limited to criminal contexts. **2.** Students may say drug testing would be appropriate in cases of reasonable suspicion, but not in "blanket searches."

**Chapter 4, p. 5**

**1.** Answers will vary, but should show an understanding that the text of the Constitution is often insufficient by itself to provide a clear resolution to difficult constitutional questions. Additional information—such as prior Supreme Court decisions, historical information, and other writings by the authors of the Constitution—may help suggest which answer is better. **2.** Congress can create financial incentives for State and local governments to participate in federally sponsored projects. Receipt of federal funding can depend on State and local compliance with federal requirements. For example, States must fulfill federal requirements in order to receive federal funds for highway safety programs.

**Chapter 5, p. 6**

**1.** Answers will vary, but should reflect understanding that the States have great autonomy to govern themselves and to structure their own electoral process, but that the Constitution also imposes certain overriding requirements that all States must obey. **2.** Answers will vary, but should involve a comparison of the strength of the constitutional rights presented in the three cases. Some students might argue that the Constitution gives a high level of protection to the Bill of Rights values of free speech and personal privacy (*Whitcomb* and *Chandler*), but less protection for the status of being an ex-felon (*Richardson*).

**Chapter 6, p. 7**

**1.** Answers will vary, but should reflect recognition that discrimination based on race or gender is not acceptable in American law and society. Discrimination against people under 21 is not as universally opposed—perhaps because people's race or gender will not change, but their age will. **2.** While the States won control in deciding voting requirements in State elections, it became too difficult to keep track of who could vote in national elections but not in State elections.

**Chapter 7, p. 8**

**1.** The Court ruled that reasonable limits on campaign contributions do not violate First Amendment rights, since limits do not keep candidates from raising the money they need to communicate with voters. The Court could also have found that First Amendment rights outweigh governmental interests in controlling election behavior, and could have allowed unlimited contributions. **2.** Because the Supreme Court is the highest court, no other court can overturn its decisions. If, over time, a decision proves to be unwise or incorrect, it is up to the Court to recognize that and to overrule the erroneous or out-of-date decision when the opportunity arises.

**Chapter 8, p. 9**

**1.** Newspapers can still be sued for defamation; *Tornillo* only determined that the papers could not be forced by statute to print the individual's reply. To prove defamation, however, a public figure such as a candidate must show that the article was both false and printed with "actual malice," meaning either actual knowledge of its falsity or reckless disregard of the truth. **2.** Stations may well have refused to carry controversial talk show hosts if they were required to make time available for others to air opposing points of view.

**Chapter 9, p. 10**

**1.** Under the rule of *Flast*, the federal court must carefully analyze in each case the nature of the governmental action and the basis of the taxpayer's interest being asserted. In this case, the taxpayers did have standing if their First

© Prentice-Hall, Inc.

Amendment rights were being violated. **2.** By focusing on standing, the Supreme Court and other courts are attempting to decide which kinds of issues are within their jurisdiction to decide. This is important because Article III of the Constitution gives the Supreme Court only limited jurisdiction; the Court cannot decide a matter unless it is properly within its constitutional power. This restriction keeps the courts from interfering in areas that the Constitution assigns to other branches of government.

**Chapter 10, p. 11**

**1.** The Court's decision created a distinction between legislative functions, which are protected, and other activities, such as communicating with constituents. The Court leaves members of Congress at risk of being sued for these other activities. **2.** Justice Brennan cited a similar case from English history in which Sir William, Speaker of the House of Commons, was sued for statements about Charles II. A provision in the English Bill of Rights was created to protect freedom of speech and debate in the legislature.

**Chapter 11, p. 12**

**1.** The Federal Government has only those powers that are specifically assigned to it under the Constitution, and cannot adopt legislation that is not within its power. The Commerce Clause is one source of federal authority. **2.** The Court did not find it to be an issue of interstate commerce. In fact, the Court ruled that New Jersey's public accommodations law infringed the Boy Scouts' freedom of expressive association and interfered with their right to oppose homosexual conduct.

**Chapter 12, p. 13**

**1.** The congressional subcommittee did not give Watkins a fair opportunity to determine if he could lawfully refuse to answer questions. The Court's decision was rooted in the protection provided by the Fifth Amendment's due process clause. **2.** There was widespread fear about the international rise of communism and the extent to which Communists and sympathizers might have infiltrated the government. The House Un-American Activities Committee conducted extensive inquiries into the influence of Communists in the United States.

**Chapter 13, p. 14**

**1.** The cases are similar in that a President allegedly did something harmful to a citizen. But in the *Clinton* case, the President's actions were not part of his official duty as President and they occurred before he became President. Nixon's actions were part of his official duty as President. The Court's distinctions are valid. **2.** Answers will vary but should recognize that the Court's balancing of interests does give the President great leeway and does prevent the individuals most affected from taking direct legal action against him. The majority notes that other forces influencing the President's behavior include the congressional inquiry and the potential for impeachment, the scrutiny of the press, and perhaps the desire to be reelected.

**Chapter 14, p. 15**

**1.** Answers will vary, depending on whether students agreed or disagreed with Justice Black. Students' answers should weigh the needs of national security against the rights of citizens. **2.** Some students might think that it is appropriate for justices to consider the times when they include national emergencies or other extreme situations in which not considering them could result in a wrong decision. Other students might think that justices should strive to base their decisions on legal precedent only, ignoring the circumstances of the times.

**Chapter 15, p. 16**

**1.** Answers will vary, but should show an appreciation of both Justice Brennan's argument about the importance of welfare to the individual recipient and Justice Black's argument about the importance to the government of being able to terminate ineligible recipients quickly and inexpensively. **2.** Answers will vary, but should reflect Justice Brennan's reasoning in *Goldberg* that welfare is special, because it helps poor people to meet their basic needs.

**Chapter 16, p. 17**

**1.** Answers will vary, but should reflect an understanding of the reasoning undertaken by each justice in coming to a conclusion. Justice O'Connor states that with certain "safeguards" government aid on a "neutral basis" is not an endorsement of religion. Justice Souter argued that earlier cases had held that such programs did subsidize religious education by freeing funds the religious school would have used. **2.** Between *Aguilar* (1985) and *Agostini* (1997), the Court adopted a more flexible analysis for determining whether governmental aid violates the Establishment Clause.

**Chapter 17, p. 18**

**1.** Justice Rehnquist accepted the finding because Congress had conducted extensive hearings and is the body authorized under the Constitution to raise an army. Justices White and Marshall argued that the indisputable facts—including the large number of women currently in the armed services—undercut Congress's determination. **2.** The changing nature of warfare, particularly the increased use of technology, makes gender less significant. Moreover, some women are physically strong, just as some men are not. Laws that are based on stereotypical assumptions about gender-based capabilities are suspect, and should be closely scrutinized.

© Prentice-Hall, Inc.

# Answer Key

**Chapter 18, p. 19**
**1.** The Court found that the activity regulated by the DPPA–distribution of drivers' personal information–had a direct impact on interstate commerce and did not involve the States' sovereign functions in governing their citizens. **2.** Rehnquist was discussing the issues of federalism, of what pertains to the National Government and what pertains to the States—issues that have been at the heart of United States legal history since the Constitution's ratification.

**Chapter 19, p. 20**
**1.** The armband was "symbolic speech," intended to communicate an opinion on a current topic of public debate. **2.** Answers will vary, but should recognize that *Tinker* involved symbolic speech that the Court saw as not disruptive to education. In *Tinker*, too, the school appeared to be punishing the expression of politically unpopular ideas. By contrast, *Fraser* and *Kuhlmeier* involved explicit speech on subjects that school officials found inappropriate for discussion in school-sponsored activities, such as assembly or student newspapers. **3.** The main facts that they took into account were the facts that the protest was silent, it did not infringe upon the rights of others, and it did not interfere with the school's work.

**Chapter 20, p. 21**
**1.** The majority recognized that there could be legitimate reasons for flight and was therefore not willing to conclude that flight always justified a stop. **2.** Justices Stevens and Marshall would probably say that innocent people, particularly minorities, in high-crime areas may also have valid reasons for wishing to avoid contact with the police, so that running would not provide grounds for a stop under the Fourth Amendment.

**Chapter 21, p. 22**
**1.** Justice Marshall felt that the purpose of affirmative action had not yet been realized, that the wrongs of a long history of discrimination had not yet been made right. **2.** The *Bakke* case was based specifically on the school's use of race as a factor, and would not itself prohibit consideration of other social or economic criteria.

**Chapter 22, p. 23**
**1.** Although Justice Stevens recognized the appropriateness of the congressional goal, he found that the means chosen to achieve the goal violated the First Amendment because they were too broadly applied, infringing on the First Amendment rights of adults. **2.** Some students might think it is important to make such distinctions because access to different forms of media, and their audience and availability, make it impossible to apply the First Amendment equally to all forms. Other students might think that an expression is an expression in any form, so the First Amendment should be applied equally to all forms of expression.

**Chapter 23, p. 24**
**1.** No, the decision only prohibits State enforcement of that contract. This means the parties could agree to the racial provision but could not sue if someone violated it. However, fair housing laws now prohibit discrimination in the sale of housing. **2.** Answers will vary but should recognize that the Constitution generally imposes limits on governmental behavior. State and federal laws have restricted individuals' rights to take a variety of economic activities (like selling a house or hiring an employee) because of someone's race, color, gender, religion, or national origin.

**Chapter 24, p. 25**
**1.** He felt that while the health hazard was not an immediate one, it will become one as the landfills become filled to capacity, and that previous Court decisions have allowed States to restrict laws for purposes of protecting against health hazards. **2.** Some students might agree with Justice Stewart's argument that waste is commerce regardless of whether it has immediate value. Waste disposal is an industry that is valuable in many different ways, including monetarily. Others might think that because waste has no value and is potentially harmful, it should not be considered commerce.

**Chapter 25, p. 26**
**1.** The Court in *Morris* looked to whether the Board was exercising significant legislative functions. Thus, there could be elected bodies with civic, charitable, social or business functions that were not sufficiently legislative. **2.** While each of the nineteen towns had one elected board members, those elected from larger towns had votes that were weighted more than the votes of board members from smaller towns.

## Landmark Cases

***McCulloch* v. *Maryland*, p. 28**
**1.** The words refer to any action that is not prohibited, that is taken in the spirit of the Constitution, and has a legitimate purpose. **2.** The decision established the supremacy of the Constitution, as well as the Constitution's flexibility.

***Gibbons* v. *Ogden*, p. 30**
**1.** An advocate of States' rights would want to have a narrow view of the commerce power so that States could have more power over the business they conducted. A national supremacy partisan would want the Federal Government to have more power to regulate business in States, which is possible with a broader view. **2.** Federal regulation of railways, airlines, pipelines, television stations, telephone communication, and racial segregation have their foundation in the *Gibbons* case.

© Prentice Hall, Inc.

*Dred Scott* v. *Sandford,* p. 32
**1.** The decision was rendered in a time when many people, both operating within and under the Federal Government, believed that African Americans were considered property rather than citizens. The decision reflects the many sentiments of the people of the time. **2.** Taney might have anticipated disputes that also involved the issue of slavery in the territories and, therefore, took the opportunity to address the issue.

*Civil Rights Cases,* p. 34
**1.** The reasoning is a narrow construction because the Court considered their power over private property matters to be very limited. **2.** Restricting the rights of African Americans because of their race would continue to deny them the rights of citizenship. **3.** Those who think private behavior should be subject to government regulation might think it should only be limited when it has an impact on the well-being of others. Those in favor of no regulation might think the government should not interfere under any circumstances.

*Plessy* v. *Ferguson,* p. 36
**1.** Students who find a flaw might point out that political and civil equality are part of social equality and vice versa. They are not separate. **2.** This explanation is correct to some extent because the Court took a hands-off approach and allowed the situation in the South to continue as the majority of its residents wanted it to.

*Schenck* v. *United States,* p. 38
**1.** Some students might think the test is reasonable while others might think there are more reasonable ways to balance free speech and national security. **2.** Some students might think Schenck's actions did present a real danger because the letters could have encouraged men to dodge the draft, leaving the army with fewer soldiers to use in battle; they could have also lowered morale. Others might think his actions did not present a real danger because there was such a small number of letters, relative to the number of people being drafted, that the war effort would not be affected.

*Powell* v. *Alabama,* p. 40
**1.** The right to counsel includes adequate time to obtain counsel and time to prepare a defense with counsel. **2.** The exact nature of the right to counsel can still be determined by the States in State court cases.

*Brown* v. *Board of Education of Topeka,* p. 42
**1.** A unanimous decision was essential so that people would be more accepting of the decision and more ready to work toward eliminating segregation. A dissenting vote might have served as encouragement for segregation supporters to continue to fight for segregation. **2.** Answers may vary. Students might say that Warren's strongest argument was essentially his argument that segregation denies equal protection because it inhibits children's ability to learn by making them feel inferior.

*Mapp* v. *Ohio,* p. 44
**1.** By urging judicial restraint, Justice Harlan was asking the Court to play a smaller role in society. He felt the Court's decision amounted to judicial activism; the Court was playing too large of a role in societal affairs. Students will either agree with Justice Harlan or Justice Clark. **2.** The 14th Amendment gives the Supreme Court the power to nullify any State action or legislation that strips citizens of privileges or immunities. Therefore, it allowed the Court to step in and force Ohio to provide Mapp with the 4th Amendment protection to which she has a constitutional right. **3.** Students who think criminals should be released when a procedural error takes place might think that procedural errors impair the right to a fair and accurate trial. Students who think criminals should not be released might think that if the criminal is proven guilty, the criminal should still be punished despite the error.

*Engel* v. *Vitale,* p. 46
**1.** Some students might think that the 1st Amendment provides for the separation of church and state by explicitly giving Congress no power to regulate religion. Something that cannot be regulated by the state should have no connection with the state. Others might think that although the amendment provides for no state regulation, it does not necessarily mean that the church has no place in state activities. **2.** Yes, the Court took both clauses into account. Some students might agree with Black while others might think the decision is antireligious.

*Miranda* v. *Arizona,* p. 48
**1.** A person might not know all the rights the accused have during police interrogation. Also, information from the interrogation can be used in the trial. **2.** Some students might think individual rights are paramount in keeping with the spirit of the 5th and 6th amendments among other provisions of the Constitution. Others might think that the public safety should outweigh individual rights; therefore, anything that might interfere with an investigation should be avoided.

*New York Times Co.* v. *United States,* p. 50
**1.** Prior restraint constitutes a punishment before an act takes place while punishment after publication allows the act to take place first. **2.** Some students might think that prior restraint should be disallowed under all circumstances. Others might think that it should be allowed under some circumstances such as when national security

© Prentice-Hall, Inc.

# Answer Key

would be threatened by publication, or possibly when publication of material could interfere with the right to a fair trial or some other level of the judicial process.

*Roe* v. *Wade,* p. 52
**1.** Some students might think the Constitution does not guarantee a right to privacy because it does not use these words specifically. Those that do think the Constitution provides this guarantee might identify the source as the Bill of Rights or the 14th Amendment. Students might think that the right should be protected in a variety of circumstances, possibly including abortion decisions, family relations, and celebrity's rights to some privacy. **2.** Some students might think abortion should fall under the police power either by regulating it so that it is safe and available or by declaring it an illegal, punishable offense. Others might think abortion does not fall under the police power at all because it is a private, medical decision made by an individual.

*United States* v. *Nixon,* p. 54
**1.** Students may think the outcome would have been the same because revealing the content of the tapes would not pose a threat to national security. Students may think the outcome would have been different because revealing conversations between the President and top officials would threaten national security. **2.** Students might think executive privilege can be claimed when the President is dealing with defense information, when the President is in the midst of trying to come to formal trade agreements with other nations and the release of negotiation information could affect the outcome, or in a variety of other situations. **3.** Students might agree or disagree that Nixon violated those people's rights to privacy, equal protection, and protection against unreasonable seizures, as provided for by the 4th and 14th Amendments.

*New Jersey* v. *T.L.O.,* p. 56
**1.** Some students might think the standard strikes the right balance because school officials may need a little more freedom to act in order to keep the school setting suitable for learning. Others might think an improper balance was struck because students' rights to privacy are considered less important than the rights of others. **2.** Some students might think it should be limited to these cases because they are the only ones that involve a serious threat to others. Other students might think warrantless searches can be conducted in less severe situations.

*Cruzan* v. *Director, Missouri Dept. of Health,* p. 58
**1.** Both cases involved the rights of an individual person or group to make a decision without interference from the government. In *Roe* the issue was privacy, but in *Cruzan* the justices focused on the issue of liberty in making the ruling. Answers will vary, but some students might think the justices may have approached the cases differently because of their interpretation of the word "person" in the 14th Amendment. Some students might agree with basing the rulings on this distinction while others might think the difference is invalid. **2.** Some students might think a living will is the only thing that constitutes "clear and convincing evidence." Some might think that any account family members can provide as to the suffering person's wishes can be considered "clear and convincing evidence." Some students might think only next of kin can decide, some might think only medical-care providers can decide, and some might think neither or a combination of both can decide.

**Photograph Credits**

**page 28** CORBIS; **page 30** Bettman/CORBIS; **page 32** CORBIS; **page 34** AP Photo/Staff; **page 36** AP Photo/Horace Cort; **page 38** Bettman/CORBIS; **page40** Bettman/CORBIS; **page 42** Michelle Bridwell/PictureQuest; **page 44** Reuters NewMedia Inc./CORBIS; **page 46** Oscar White/CORBIS; **page 48** Bettman/CORBIS; **page 50** CORBIS; **page 51** AP Photo; **page 52** AP Photo/Tim Sharp (left), AP Photo (right); **page 54** AP Photo; **page 56** AP Photo/Dan Loh/Pool; **page 56** B. Markel/Liaison Agency

© Prentice-Hall, Inc.